CGP has autumn term Maths conkered!

Ah, autumn. The season of mists, mellow fruitfulness and Maths practice. And if you're looking for Maths, you've come to the right place...

This brilliant CGP book gathers a huge range of skills from the Year 3 curriculum — there's a page of practice for every day of the autumn term.

It's perfect for use in class or at home, with plenty of examples and colourful pictures to keep pupils interested. It's not to be mist!

What CGP is all about

Our sole aim here at CGP is to produce the highest quality books — carefully written, immaculately presented and dangerously close to being funny.

Then we work our socks off to get them out to you — at the cheapest possible prices.

Contents

☑ Use the tick boxes to help keep a record of which tests have been attempted.

Published by CGP

ISBN: 978 1 78908 649 2

Editors: Tom Carney, Georgina Fairclough, Joe Shaw, Sarah Williams

With thanks to Emma Chambers and Emma Clayton for the proofreading.

With thanks to Lottie Edwards for the copyright research.

Clipart from Corel®

1 pence coin © iStock.com/coopder1
2 pence coin © iStock.com/peterspiro
5p coin © iStock.com/duncan1890
10 pence coin © iStock.com/john shepherd
20 pence coin © iStock.com/Jaap2
50 pence coin © iStock.com/duncan1890

Printed by Elanders Ltd, Newcastle upon Tyne.
Based on the classic CGP style created by Richard Parsons.

How to Use this Book

- This book contains <u>60 daily practice tests</u>.

- We've split them into <u>12 sections</u> — that's roughly one for <u>each week</u> of the Year 3 <u>autumn term</u>.

- Each week is made up of <u>5 tests</u>, so there's one for <u>every school day</u> of the term (Monday — Friday).

- Each test should take about <u>10 minutes</u> to complete.

- The tests contain a <u>mix</u> of topics from <u>Year 2</u> and <u>Year 3</u> Maths. <u>New Year 3 topics</u> are gradually introduced as you go through the book.

- The tests <u>increase in difficulty</u> as you progress through the term.

- Each test looks something like this:

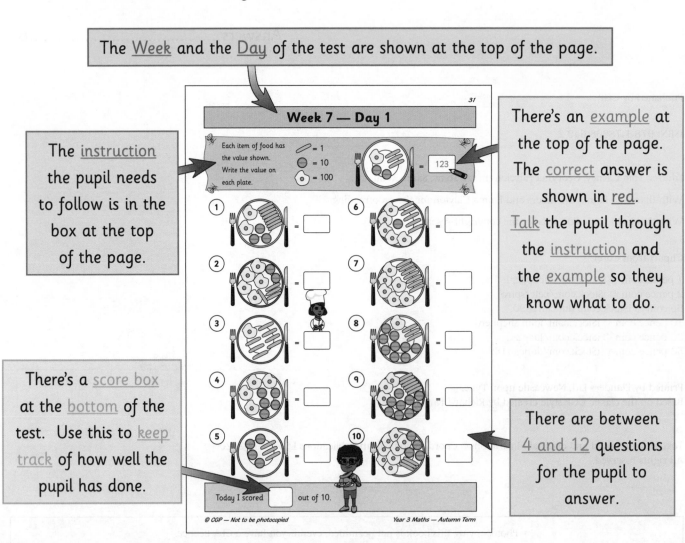

The <u>Week</u> and the <u>Day</u> of the test are shown at the top of the page.

The <u>instruction</u> the pupil needs to follow is in the box at the top of the page.

There's an <u>example</u> at the top of the page. The <u>correct</u> answer is shown in <u>red</u>. <u>Talk</u> the pupil through the <u>instruction</u> and the <u>example</u> so they know what to do.

There's a <u>score box</u> at the <u>bottom</u> of the test. Use this to <u>keep track</u> of how well the pupil has done.

There are between <u>4 and 12</u> questions for the pupil to answer.

Week 1 — Day 1

Complete the sentence.   22 more than 11 is [33]

1 17 more than 20 is [ ]

2 23 more than 15 is [ ]

3 36 more than 21 is [ ]

4 12 less than 24 is [ ]

5 30 less than 49 is [ ]

6 22 less than 55 is [ ]

7 12 more than 18 is [ ]

8 27 more than 25 is [ ]

9 49 more than 21 is [ ]

10 18 less than 25 is [ ]

11 24 less than 42 is [ ]

12 25 less than 64 is [ ]

Today I scored [ ] out of 12.

Year 3 Maths — Autumn Term

Week 1 — Day 2

Draw hands on the clock to show the correct time.

ten past nine

1. half past seven

2. quarter past ten

3. ten past four

4. quarter to five

5. five past six

6. twenty past eleven

7. twenty-five past one

8. quarter to twelve

9. five to eight

10. twenty to two

Today I scored [ ] out of 10.

Week 1 — Day 3

Name the 3D shape.

How many vertices does the shape have?

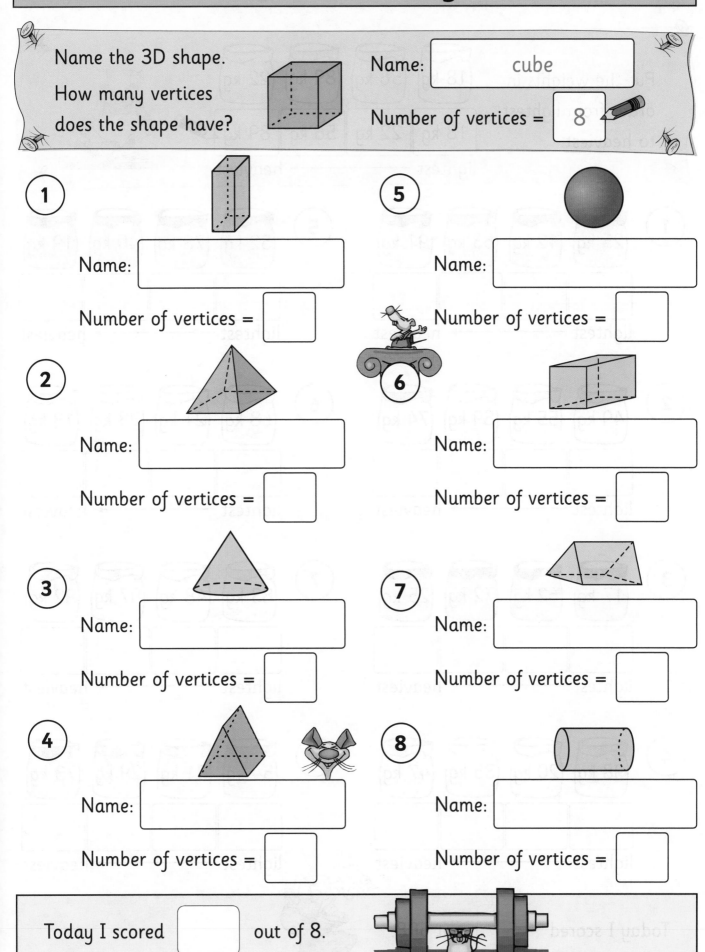

Name: cube

Number of vertices = 8

1

Name:

Number of vertices =

2

Name:

Number of vertices =

3

Name:

Number of vertices =

4

Name:

Number of vertices =

5

Name:

Number of vertices =

6

Name:

Number of vertices =

7

Name:

Number of vertices =

8

Name:

Number of vertices =

Today I scored [   ] out of 8.

Year 3 Maths — Autumn Term

Week 1 — Day 4

Put the weights in order from lightest to heaviest.

| 18 kg | 56 kg | 89 kg | 22 kg |

| 18 kg | 22 kg | 56 kg | 89 kg |

lightest ⟶ heaviest

1

| 25 kg | 12 kg | 53 kg | 91 kg |

lightest ⟶ heaviest

2

| 49 kg | 55 kg | 89 kg | 74 kg |

lightest ⟶ heaviest

3

| 17 kg | 62 kg | 72 kg | 25 kg |

lightest ⟶ heaviest

4

| 98 kg | 20 kg | 35 kg | 47 kg |

lightest ⟶ heaviest

5

| 52 kg | 78 kg | 40 kg | 19 kg |

lightest ⟶ heaviest

6

| 68 kg | 21 kg | 38 kg | 13 kg |

lightest ⟶ heaviest

7

| 83 kg | 48 kg | 97 kg | 92 kg |

lightest ⟶ heaviest

8

| 54 kg | 81 kg | 29 kg | 73 kg |

lightest ⟶ heaviest

Today I scored [ ] out of 8.

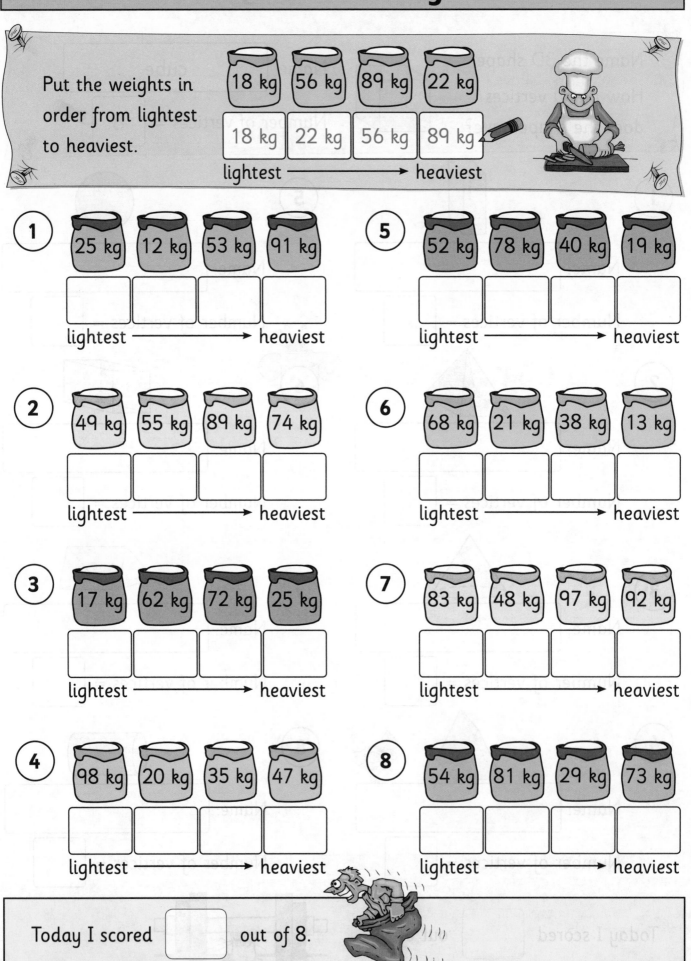

Week 1 — Day 5

How many slices of cake are there in total?

There are 3 cakes.
Each cake is cut into 10 slices.

Total = 30 slices

1 There are 5 cakes.
Each cake is cut into 2 slices.

Total = [ ] slices

2 There are 6 cakes.
Each cake is cut into 10 slices.

Total = [ ] slices

3 There are 3 cakes.
Each cake is cut into 5 slices.

Total = [ ] slices

4 There are 7 cakes.
Each cake is cut into 10 slices.

Total = [ ] slices

5 There are 9 cakes.
Each cake is cut into 2 slices.

Total = [ ] slices

6 There are 5 cakes.
Each cake is cut into 5 slices.

Total = [ ] slices

7 There are 11 cakes.
Each cake is cut into 2 slices.

Total = [ ] slices

8 There are 10 cakes.
Each cake is cut into 10 slices.

Total = [ ] slices

9 There are 12 cakes.
Each cake is cut into 5 slices.

Total = [ ] slices

10 There are 11 cakes.
Each cake is cut into 10 slices.

Total = [ ] slices

Today I scored [ ] out of 10.

Year 3 Maths — Autumn Term

Week 2 — Day 1

What fraction of the fruits have had a bite taken out of them?

$\dfrac{1}{2}$

1

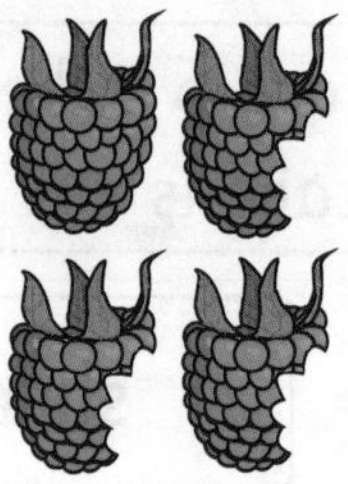

2

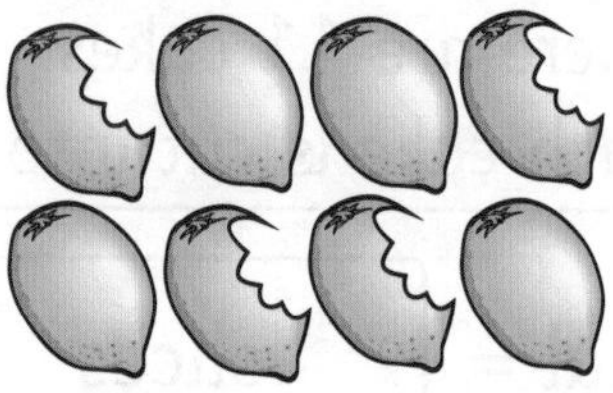

3

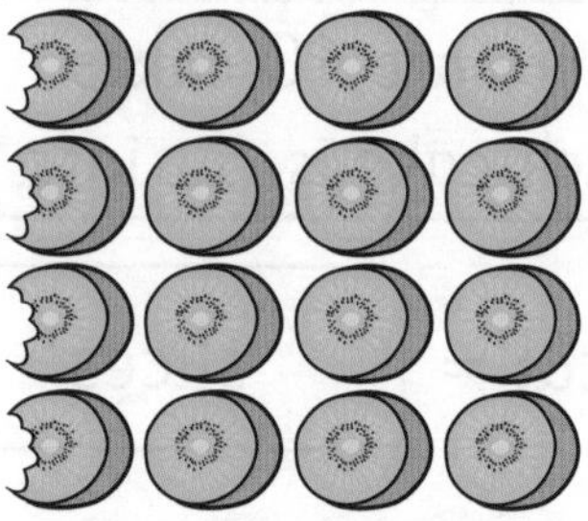

4

5

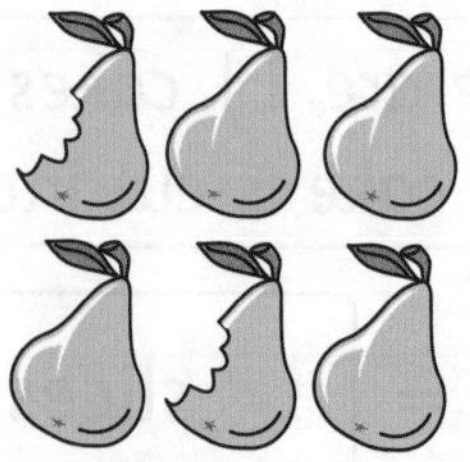

6

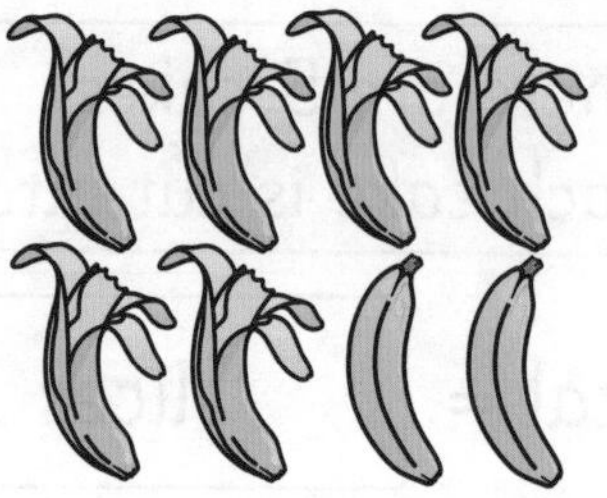

7

8

9

10

Today I scored [ ] out of 10.

Week 2 — Day 2

Fill in the missing numbers in this number sequence.

18   16   14   [12]   [10]

1 44   34   24   ☐   ☐

6 27   30   ☐   ☐   39

2 25   20   15   ☐   ☐

7 71   ☐   ☐   41   31

3 6   9   12   ☐   ☐

8 95   ☐   85   80   ☐

4 30   28   26   ☐   ☐

9 ☐   79   69   ☐   49

5 72   70   ☐   ☐   64

10 ☐   38   ☐   42   44

Today I scored ☐ out of 10.

Year 3 Maths — Autumn Term

Week 2 — Day 3

A chocolate bar weighs **46 g**.

Look at the weight of the treat. Is it heavier or lighter than the chocolate bar?

What is the difference between the weight of the treat and the weight of the chocolate bar?

 6 g

It is than heavier / (lighter) than the chocolate bar.

Weight difference = 40 g

(1)  12 g

It is than heavier / lighter than the chocolate bar.

Weight difference = [ ] g

(2)  88 g

It is than heavier / lighter than the chocolate bar.

Weight difference = [ ] g

(3)  39 g

It is than heavier / lighter than the chocolate bar.

Weight difference = [ ] g

(4)  52 g

It is than heavier / lighter than the chocolate bar.

Weight difference = [ ] g

(5)  17 g

It is than heavier / lighter than the chocolate bar.

Weight difference = [ ] g

(6)  71 g

It is than heavier / lighter than the chocolate bar.

Weight difference = [ ] g

Today I scored [ ] out of 6.

Year 3 Maths — Autumn Term © *CGP — Not to be photocopied*

Week 2 — Day 4

Find the sum of
the numbers on
the rubber ducks.

1 2 3   6

1 2 3 2   ☐

2 1 4 3   ☐

3 2 2 5   ☐

4 3 4 5   ☐

5 1 3 6   ☐

6 3 3 4   ☐

7 1 9 5   ☐

8 6 9 2   ☐

9 3 5 7   ☐

10 6 7 8   ☐

11 6 6 5   ☐

12 9 8 7   ☐

Today I scored ☐ out of 12.

Year 3 Maths — Autumn Term

Week 2 — Day 5

Books cost **£2** each.

How many books can this person buy?

Lucas has £4.

He can buy | 2 | books.

---

1 Abiba has £6.

She can buy [ ] books.

6 Rafe has £16.

He can buy [ ] books.

2 Gordon has £10.

He can buy [ ] books.

7 Wan has £14.

She can buy [ ] books.

3 Sandra has £8.

She can buy [ ] books.

8 James has £22.

He can buy [ ] books.

4 Nadim has £12.

He can buy [ ] books.

9 Clare has £18.

She can buy [ ] books.

5 Daisy has £20.

She can buy [ ] books.

10 Abel has £24.

He can buy [ ] books.

Today I scored [ ] out of 10.

Week 3 — Day 1

Circle all the numbers made up of 2 odd digits.

14	(39)	18
(13)	(97)	20

1

15	10	11
12	17	19

6

47	57	58
71	35	29

2

39	26	23
16	17	21

7

41	91	38
20	73	81

3

16	31	27
12	38	30

8

95	63	38
49	14	72

4

67	34	49
25	51	50

9

53	92	82
39	75	64

5

33	28	59
46	12	22

10

81	63	77
69	45	88

Today I scored [ ] out of 10.

Week 3 — Day 2

Estimate the values on the number line.

Week 3 — Day 3

Take away the smallest number from the biggest number.

| 11 | 25 | 30 | 28 |

| 30 | − | 11 | = | 19 |

Biggest   Smallest

| 24 | 25 | 14 | 17 |

1 [ ] − [ ] = [ ]

Biggest   Smallest

| 34 | 17 | 21 | 12 |

2 [ ] − [ ] = [ ]

Biggest   Smallest

| 40 | 45 | 32 | 25 |

3 [ ] − [ ] = [ ]

Biggest   Smallest

| 50 | 37 | 42 | 49 |

4 [ ] − [ ] = [ ]

Biggest   Smallest

| 33 | 54 | 46 | 62 |

5 [ ] − [ ] = [ ]

Biggest   Smallest

| 39 | 28 | 66 | 77 |

6 [ ] − [ ] = [ ]

Biggest   Smallest

| 67 | 72 | 82 | 55 |

7 [ ] − [ ] = [ ]

Biggest   Smallest

| 94 | 88 | 72 | 69 |

8 [ ] − [ ] = [ ]

Biggest   Smallest

Today I scored [ ] out of 8.

Year 3 Maths — Autumn Term

Week 3 — Day 4

How many flowers are watered in total?

There are 2 daisies and 6 tulips.
One half are watered.

 4 flowers are watered

1 There are 8 roses and 12 tulips. One half are watered.

flowers are watered

2 There is 1 rose and 7 daisies. One quarter are watered.

flowers are watered

3 There are 4 pansies and 2 roses. One third are watered.

flowers are watered

4 There are 8 lilies and 4 daisies. One quarter are watered.

flowers are watered

5 There are 9 poppies and 3 tulips. One half are watered.

flowers are watered

6 There are 11 lilies and 5 roses. One quarter are watered.

flowers are watered

7 There are 7 roses and 5 tulips. One third are watered.

flowers are watered

8 There are 9 lilies and 7 daisies. Two quarters are watered.

flowers are watered

9 There are 6 pansies and 6 roses. Three quarters are watered.

flowers are watered

10 There are 9 roses and 15 daisies. Three quarters are watered.

flowers are watered

Today I scored [ ] out of 10.

Week 3 — Day 5

Micah is animal spotting in his garden. The number of each type of animal he sees is shown in the pictogram. How many animals did he see in total?

Animal	Number Seen
Snail	
Slug	
Bumblebee	

Key:
= 2 animals

14 animals in total.

1

Animal	Number Seen
Ladybird	
Honey Bee	
Wasp	

animals in total.

4

Animal	Number Seen
Fly	
Beetle	
Moth	
Centipede	

animals in total.

2

Animal	Number Seen
Centipede	
Woodlouse	
Beetle	

animals in total.

5

Animal	Number Seen
Bumblebee	
Caterpillar	
Snail	
Ladybird	

animals in total.

3

Animal	Number Seen
Fly	
Caterpillar	
Moth	

animals in total.

6

Animal	Number Seen
Slug	
Caterpillar	
Wasp	
Woodlouse	

animals in total.

Today I scored out of 6.

Year 3 Maths — Autumn Term

Week 4 — Day 1

Draw a vertical line of symmetry on the shape. Use a ruler.

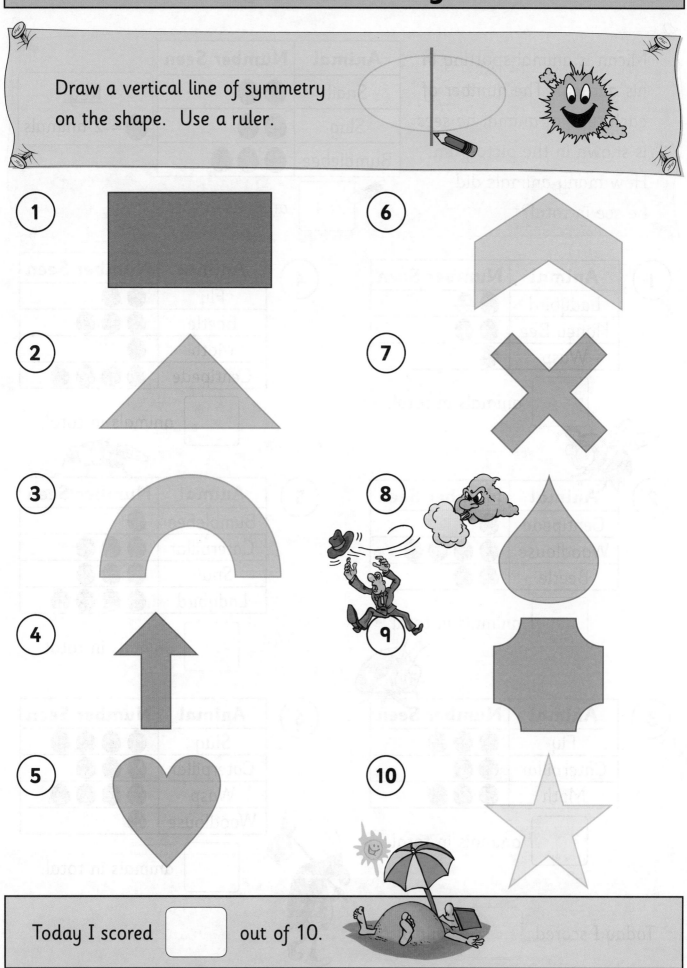

1

2

3

4

5

6

7

8

9

10

Today I scored ☐ out of 10.

Week 4 — Day 2

Write down the value of the hundreds digit and the tens digit of the number.

572

hundreds	tens
500	70

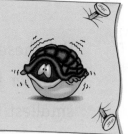

1 160 hundreds ☐ tens ☐

7 619 hundreds ☐ tens ☐

2 342 hundreds ☐ tens ☐

8 791 hundreds ☐ tens ☐

3 526 hundreds ☐ tens ☐

9 453 hundreds ☐ tens ☐

4 275 hundreds ☐ tens ☐

10 849 hundreds ☐ tens ☐

5 438 hundreds ☐ tens ☐

11 988 hundreds ☐ tens ☐

6 123 hundreds ☐ tens ☐

12 704 hundreds ☐ tens ☐

Today I scored ☐ out of 12.

Year 3 Maths — Autumn Term

Week 4 — Day 3

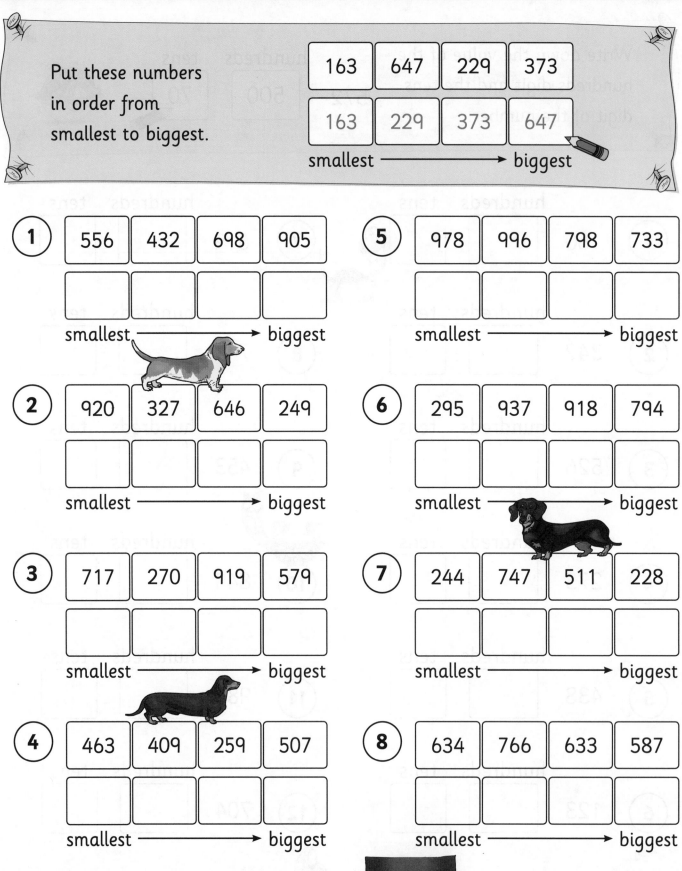

Put these numbers in order from smallest to biggest.

163	647	229	373
163	229	373	647

smallest ——————→ biggest

1 | 556 | 432 | 698 | 905 |
|---|---|---|---|
| | | | |

smallest ——————→ biggest

2 | 920 | 327 | 646 | 249 |
|---|---|---|---|
| | | | |

smallest ——————→ biggest

3 | 717 | 270 | 919 | 579 |
|---|---|---|---|
| | | | |

smallest ——————→ biggest

4 | 463 | 409 | 259 | 507 |
|---|---|---|---|
| | | | |

smallest ——————→ biggest

5 | 978 | 996 | 798 | 733 |
|---|---|---|---|
| | | | |

smallest ——————→ biggest

6 | 295 | 937 | 918 | 794 |
|---|---|---|---|
| | | | |

smallest ——————→ biggest

7 | 244 | 747 | 511 | 228 |
|---|---|---|---|
| | | | |

smallest ——————→ biggest

8 | 634 | 766 | 633 | 587 |
|---|---|---|---|
| | | | |

smallest ——————→ biggest

Today I scored ☐ out of 8.

Week 4 — Day 4

Write down the reading on the scales.

15 g

1.   g

2.   g

3.   g

4.   g

5.   g

6.   g

7.   g

8.   g

Today I scored ☐ out of 8.

    Year 3 Maths — Autumn Term

Week 4 — Day 5

Ben thinks of a number. He adds 4 to it and then divides it by 5. He gets the answer shown in the box. What was Ben's original number?

Ben's answer	Ben's original number
2	6

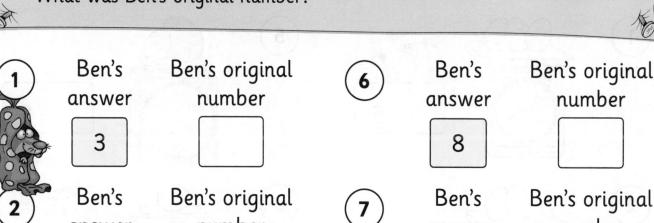

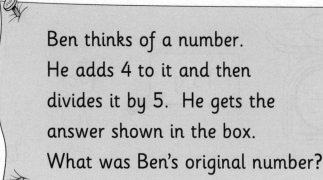

	Ben's answer	Ben's original number
1	3	
2	4	
3	6	
4	7	
5	9	

	Ben's answer	Ben's original number
6	8	
7	5	
8	1	
9	10	
10	11	

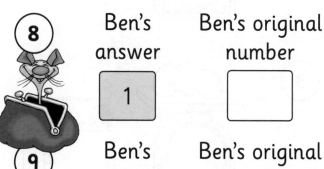

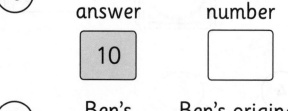

Today I scored ☐ out of 10.

Week 5 — Day 1

Write this number using digits.   One hundred and twenty three   123

1. Two hundred and forty two

7. Nine hundred and sixty five

2. One hundred and seventy six

8. Six hundred and eleven

3. Three hundred and forty two

9. Seven hundred and twenty four

4. One hundred and three

10. Five hundred and thirty nine

5. Four hundred and fifty one

11. Three hundred and eighty

6. Nine hundred and eight

12. Eight hundred and ninety three

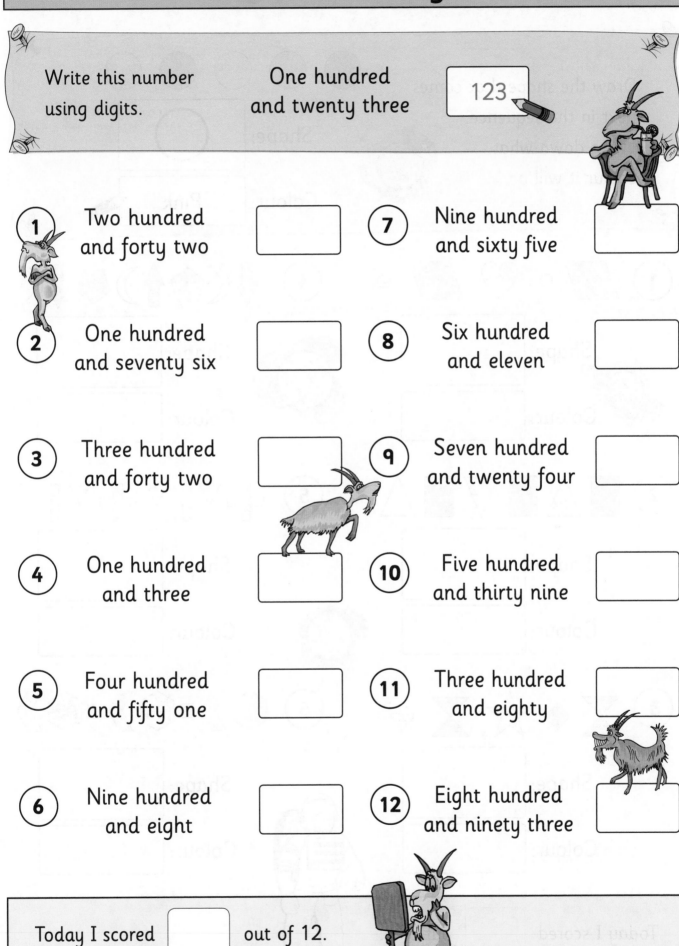

Today I scored ☐ out of 12.

Week 5 — Day 2

Draw the shape that comes next in the sequence. Write down what colour it will be.

Shape: ◯

Colour: Pink

1 Shape: _____
   Colour: _____

2 Shape: _____
   Colour: _____

3 Shape: _____
   Colour: _____

4 Shape: _____
   Colour: _____

5 Shape: _____
   Colour: _____

6 Shape: _____
   Colour: _____

Today I scored [   ] out of 6.

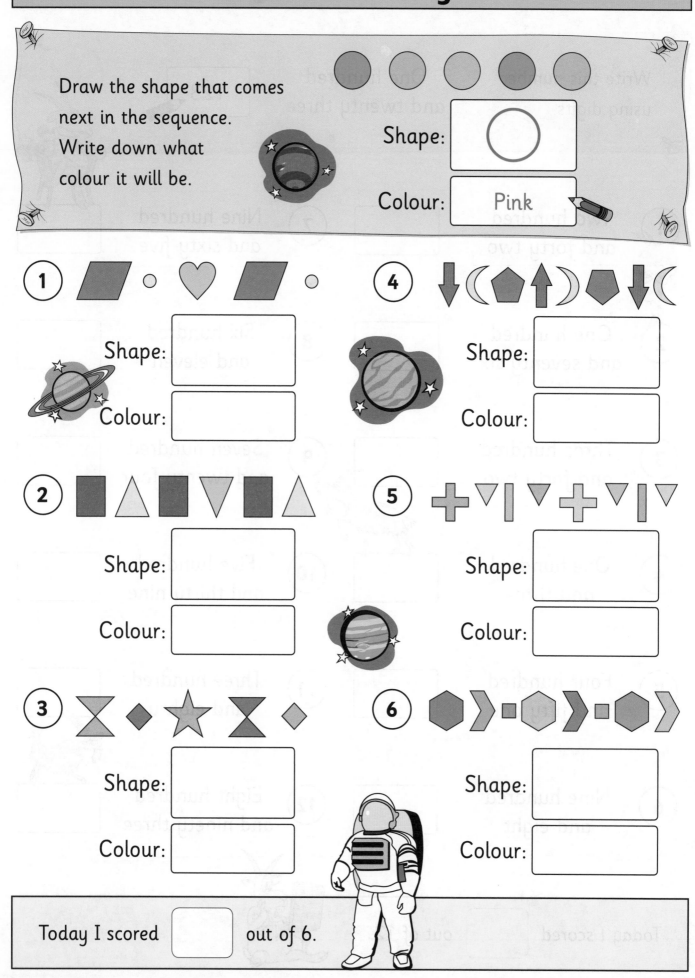

Week 5 — Day 3

Use partitioning to do the following sum.

12 + 36 = 10 + 2 + 30 + 6 = 48

(1) 37 + 22 = ☐ + ☐ + ☐ + ☐ = ☐

(2) 41 + 46 = ☐ + ☐ + ☐ + ☐ = ☐

(3) 32 + 23 = ☐ + ☐ + ☐ + ☐ = ☐

(4) 85 + 14 = ☐ + ☐ + ☐ + ☐ = ☐

(5) 63 + 17 = ☐ + ☐ + ☐ + ☐ = ☐

(6) 81 + 27 = ☐ + ☐ + ☐ + ☐ = ☐

(7) 34 + 86 = ☐ + ☐ + ☐ + ☐ = ☐

(8) 69 + 99 = ☐ + ☐ + ☐ + ☐ = ☐

Today I scored ☐ out of 8.

Year 3 Maths — Autumn Term

Week 5 — Day 4

Look at the numbers on the cards.
Draw arrows to show their
position on the number line.

| 350 | 490 |

300   400   500

1 | 750 | 850 |

700   800   900

2 | 190 | 250 |

100   200   300

3 | 140 | 220 |

100   200   300

4 | 710 | 580 |

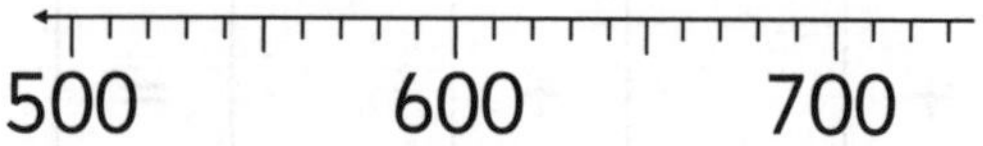

500   600   700

5 | 210 | 230 |

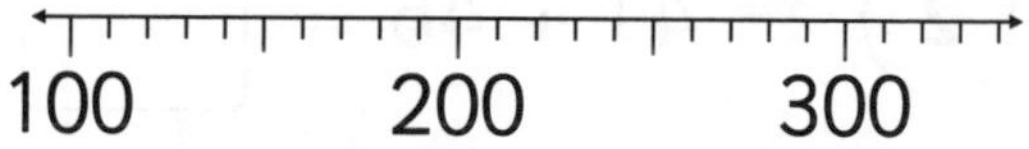

100   200   300

6 | 540 | 420 |

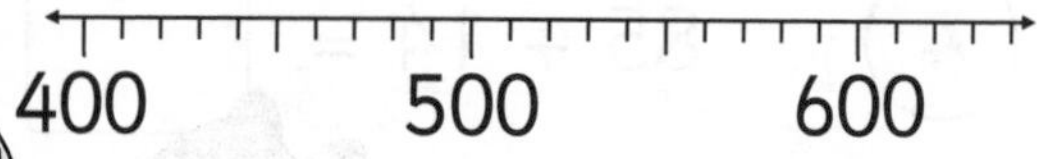

400   500   600

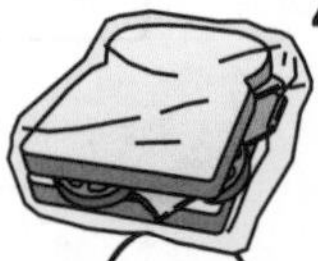

7 | 780 | 660 |

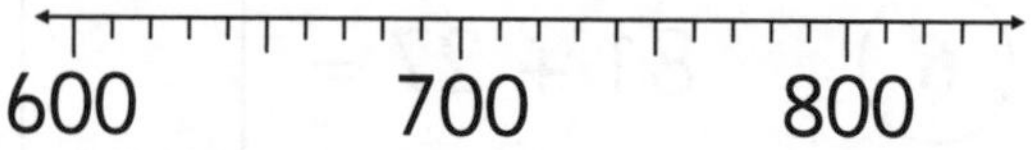

600   700   800

8 | 990 | 920 |

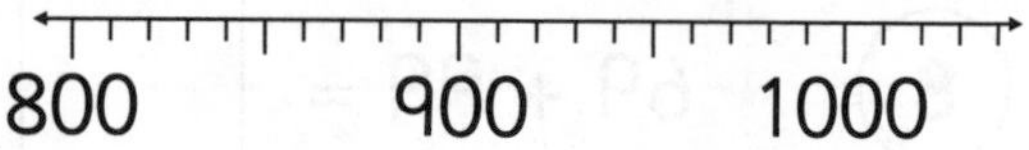

800   900   1000

Today I scored [ ] out of 8.

Week 5 — Day 5

Some children were asked to name their favourite game. The block diagram shows the results.

How many children were asked in total?

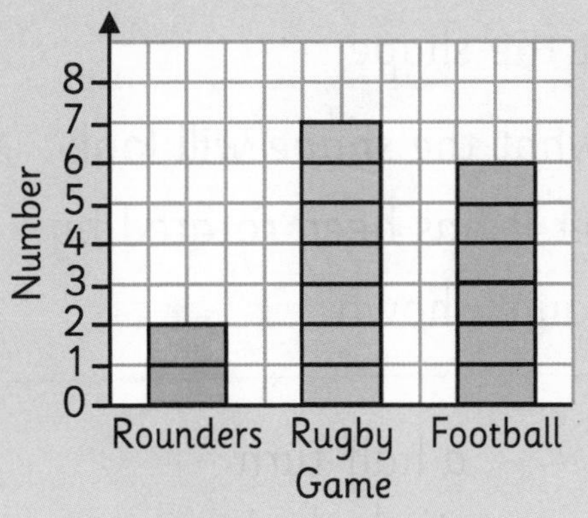

15

1

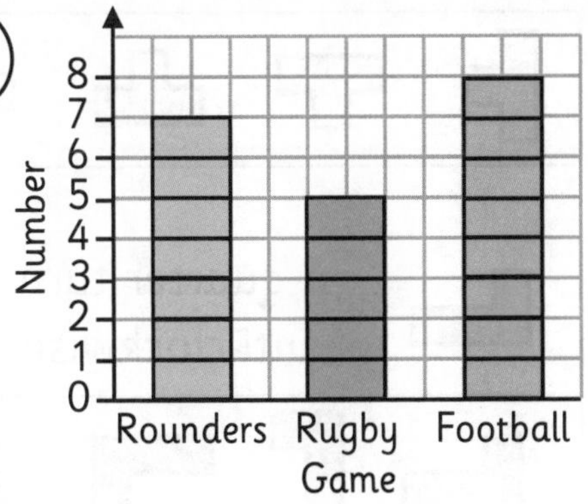

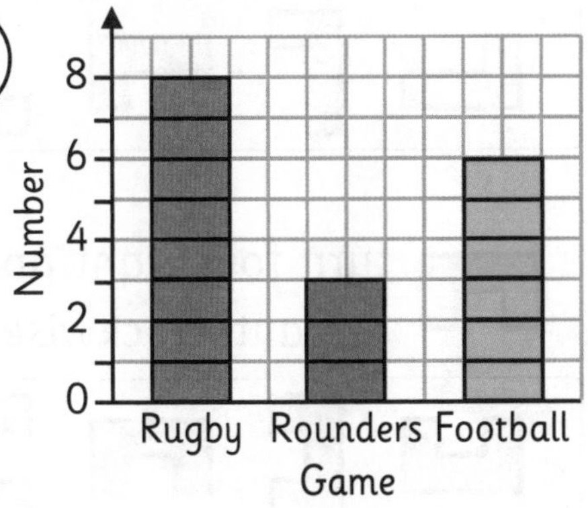

4

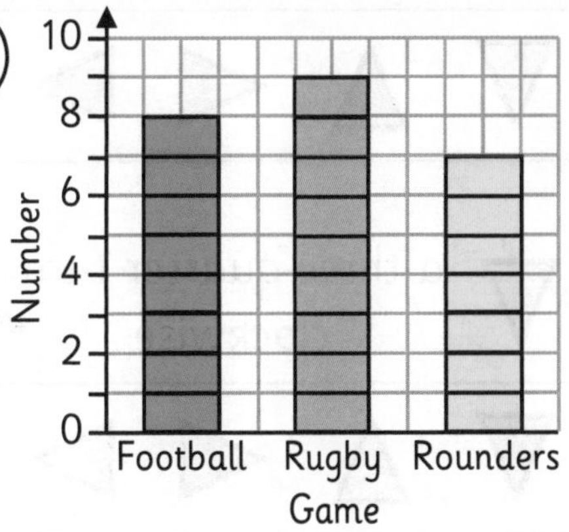

2

5

3

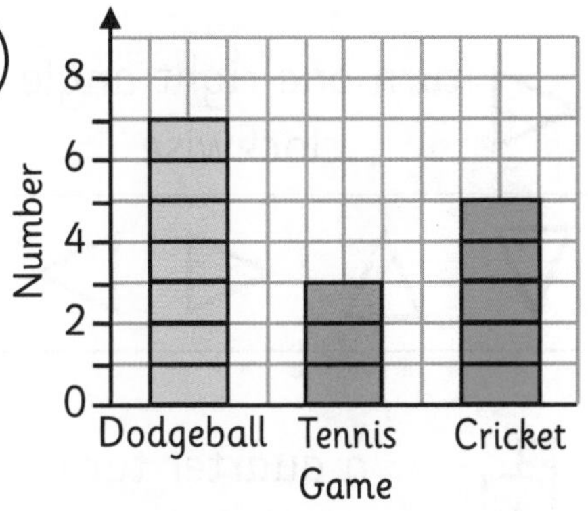

6

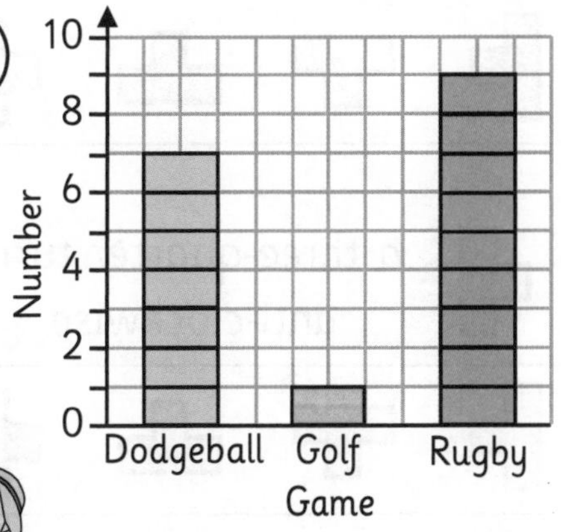

Today I scored ☐ out of 6.

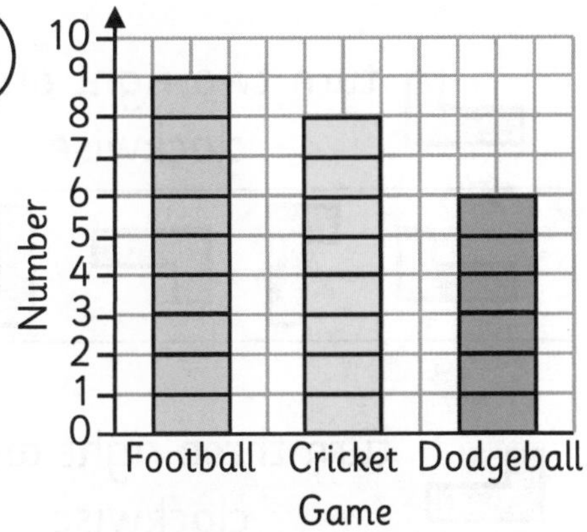

Year 3 Maths — Autumn Term

Week 6 — Day 1

Look at the shape.

Circle what the shape will look like after it has been rotated by the amount shown.

a quarter turn clockwise

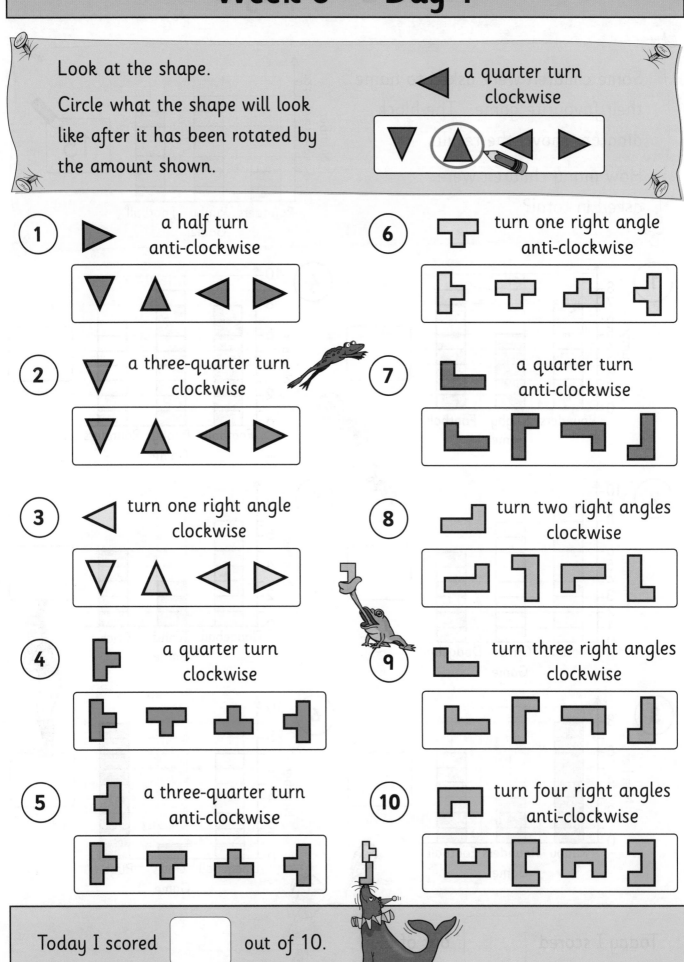

1   a half turn anti-clockwise

2   a three-quarter turn clockwise

3   turn one right angle clockwise

4   a quarter turn clockwise

5   a three-quarter turn anti-clockwise

6   turn one right angle anti-clockwise

7   a quarter turn anti-clockwise

8   turn two right angles clockwise

9   turn three right angles clockwise

10   turn four right angles anti-clockwise

Today I scored ☐ out of 10.

Week 6 — Day 2

Complete the calculation.   120 + 5 = 125

1 690 + 4 =

2 151 + 5 =

3 429 + 1 =

4 398 − 3 =

5 782 − 3 =

6 543 + 8 =

7 235 − 6 =

8 661 − 2 =

9 125 − 7 =

10 333 − 8 =

11 599 + 9 =

12 803 − 7 =

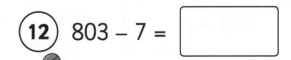

Today I scored [ ] out of 12.

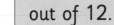

Year 3 Maths — Autumn Term

Week 6 — Day 3

Complete the calculation by filling in any gaps with 10 or 100.

$215 -$ | 10 | $= 205$

(1) $127 -$ ☐ $= 27$

(2) $356 +$ ☐ $= 366$

(3) $221 +$ ☐ $= 321$

(4) $666 -$ ☐ $= 656$

(5) $849 -$ ☐ $= 749$

(6) $583 +$ ☐ $= 593$

(7) $879 -$ ☐ $= 779$

(8) $402 -$ ☐ $= 392$

(9) $215 - 115 =$ ☐

(10) ☐ $- 50 = 50$

(11) $738 - 728 =$ ☐

(12) ☐ $- 90 =$ ☐

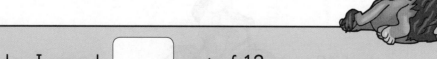

Today I scored ☐ out of 12.

Year 3 Maths — Autumn Term

© CGP — Not to be photocopied

Week 6 — Day 4

Look at the time on the blue clock.

Draw hands on the bigger clock to show the time described in the box.

10 minutes later

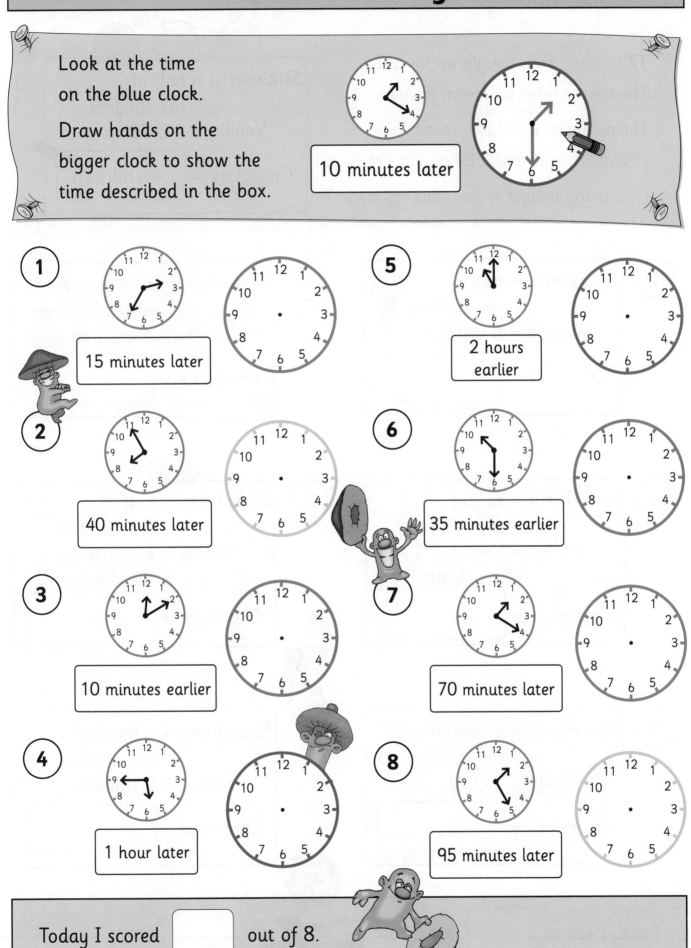

1 15 minutes later

2 40 minutes later

3 10 minutes earlier

4 1 hour later

5 2 hours earlier

6 35 minutes earlier

7 70 minutes later

8 95 minutes later

Today I scored ☐ out of 8.

Year 3 Maths — Autumn Term

Week 6 — Day 5

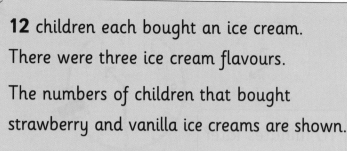

12 children each bought an ice cream.

There were three ice cream flavours.

The numbers of children that bought strawberry and vanilla ice creams are shown.

How many bought a chocolate ice cream?

Strawberry = half of the children

Vanilla = 2 children

Chocolate = 4 children

---

1 Strawberry = half of the children

Vanilla = 5 children

Chocolate =

4 Strawberry = two quarters of the children

Vanilla = 4 children

Chocolate =

2 Strawberry = half of the children

Vanilla = half of the children

Chocolate =

5 Strawberry = half of the children

Vanilla = a quarter of the children

Chocolate =

3 Strawberry = a quarter of the children

Vanilla = 1 child

Chocolate =

6 Strawberry = a third of the children

Vanilla = 2 children

Chocolate =

Today I scored ____ out of 6.

Week 7 — Day 1

Each item of food has the value shown. Write the value on each plate.

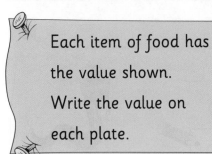

= 1

= 10

= 100

= 123

1  =

6  =

2  =

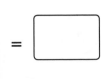

7 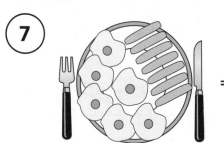 =

3  =

8  =

4  =

9  =

5  =

10  =

Today I scored ☐ out of 10.

© CGP — Not to be photocopied

Year 3 Maths — Autumn Term

Week 7 — Day 2

A toy snake is next to a centimetre scale. What is the length of the snake?

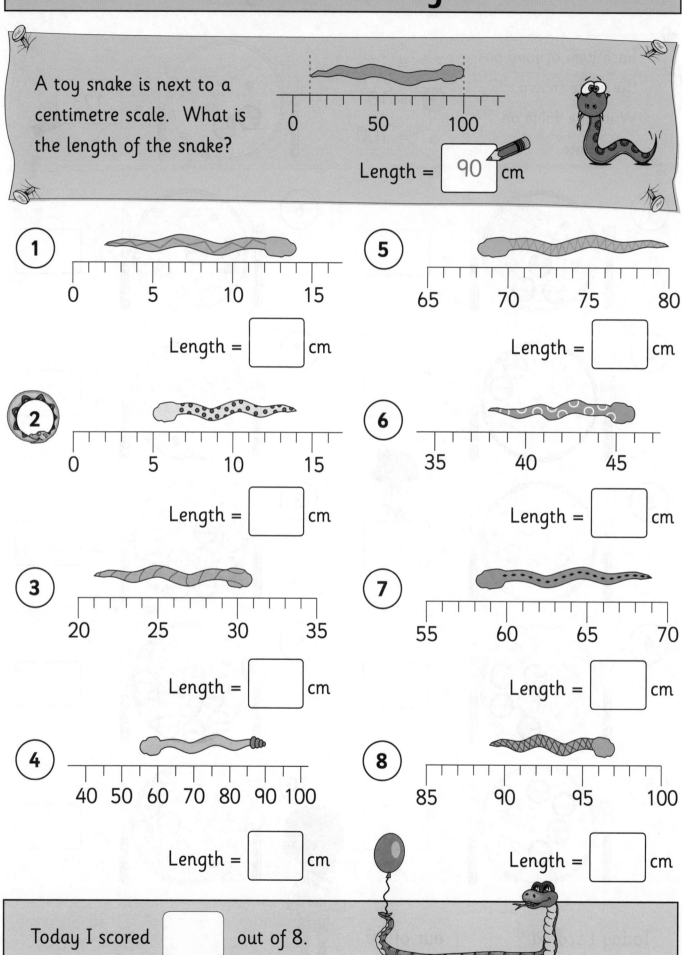

Length = 90 cm

1

Length = ☐ cm

2

Length = ☐ cm

3

Length = ☐ cm

4

Length = ☐ cm

5

Length = ☐ cm

6

Length = ☐ cm

7

Length = ☐ cm

8

Length = ☐ cm

Today I scored ☐ out of 8.

Week 7 — Day 3

Use these number cards to write the smallest 3-digit number and the largest 3-digit number that you can.

| 2 | 1 | 3 | 4 |

smallest number = 123

largest number = 432

1 | 1 | 8 | 9 | 2 |

smallest number = ☐

largest number = ☐

5 | 3 | 5 | 7 | 3 |

smallest number = ☐

largest number = ☐

2 | 2 | 3 | 7 | 6 |

smallest number = ☐

largest number = ☐

6 | 1 | 5 | 2 | 2 |

smallest number = ☐

largest number = ☐

3 | 5 | 8 | 5 | 4 |

smallest number = ☐

largest number = ☐

7 | 4 | 1 | 6 | 3 |

smallest number = ☐

largest number = ☐

4 | 9 | 1 | 3 | 2 |

smallest number = ☐

largest number = ☐

8 | 9 | 7 | 9 | 1 |

smallest number = ☐

largest number = ☐

Today I scored ☐ out of 8.

Week 7 — Day 4

Shade the fraction of the shape shown in the box.

| One half |

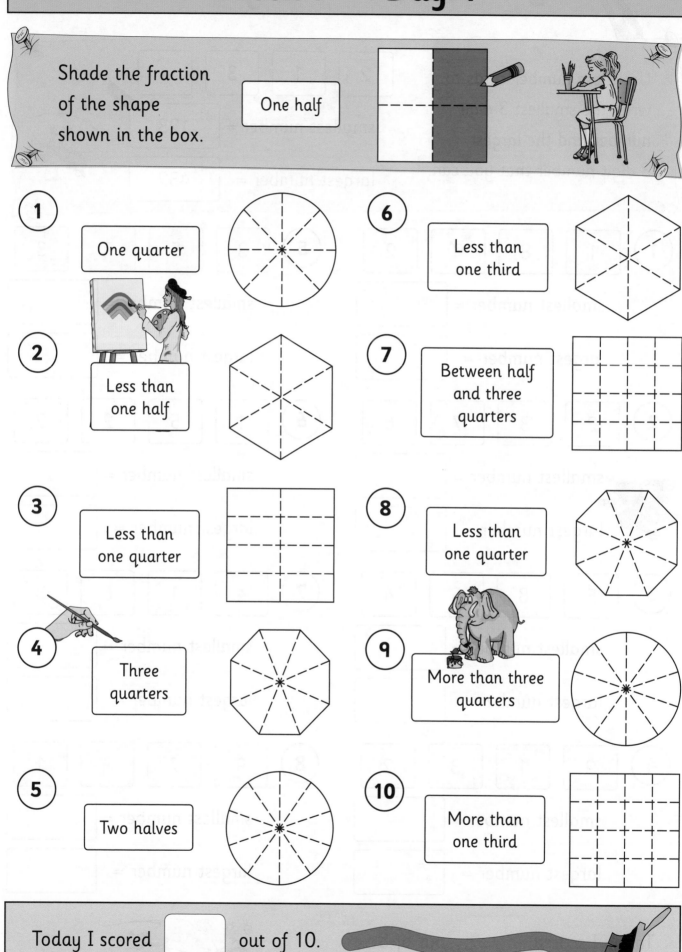

1 One quarter

2 Less than one half

3 Less than one quarter

4 Three quarters

5 Two halves

6 Less than one third

7 Between half and three quarters

8 Less than one quarter

9 More than three quarters

10 More than one third

Today I scored ☐ out of 10.

Week 7 — Day 5

Circle the container that has the largest volume.

180 ml   100 ml   **275 ml**

1
300 ml   230 ml   195 ml

2
500 l   650 l   460 l

3
440 ml   330 ml   200 ml

4
860 ml   680 ml   700 ml

5
225 l   280 l   185 l

6
765 l   770 l   757 l

7
375 ml   405 ml   430 ml

8
485 ml   499 ml   470 ml

Today I scored [   ] out of 8.

Year 3 Maths — Autumn Term

Week 8 — Day 1

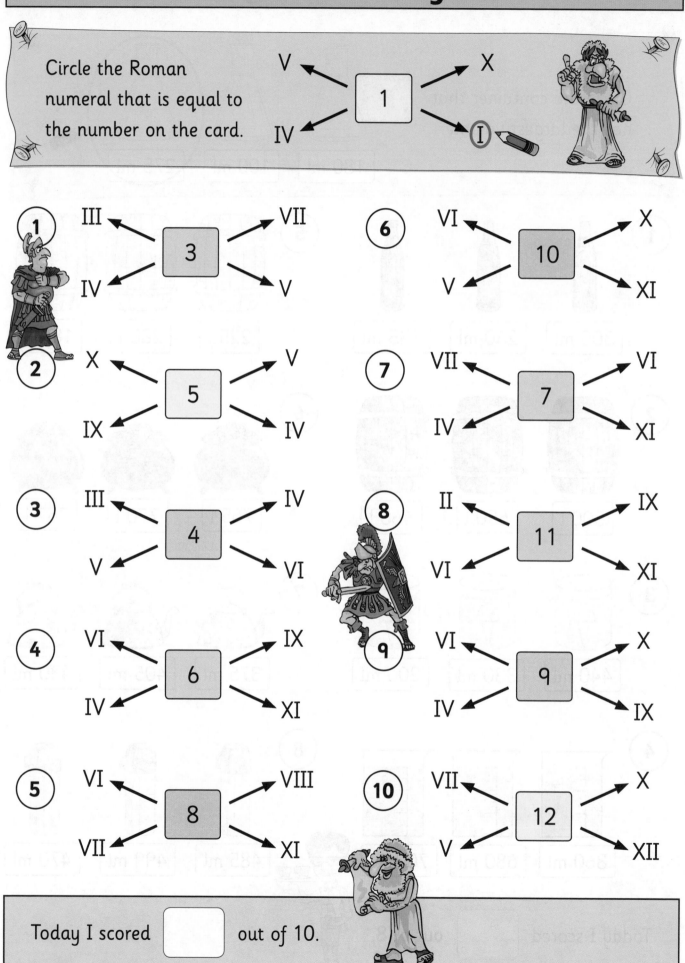

Circle the Roman numeral that is equal to the number on the card.

V ← 1 → X
IV ← 1 → I

1. III ← 3 → VII
    IV ← 3 → V

2. X ← 5 → V
    IX ← 5 → IV

3. III ← 4 → IV
    V ← 4 → VI

4. VI ← 6 → IX
    IV ← 6 → XI

5. VI ← 8 → VIII
    VII ← 8 → XI

6. VI ← 10 → X
    V ← 10 → XI

7. VII ← 7 → VI
    IV ← 7 → XI

8. II ← 11 → IX
    VI ← 11 → XI

9. VI ← 9 → X
    IV ← 9 → IX

10. VII ← 12 → X
    V ← 12 → XII

Today I scored [ ] out of 10.

Week 8 — Day 2

Write down the time shown on the clock using **am** or **pm**.

in the evening

7.00 pm

1 in the evening

2 in the evening

3 in the morning

4 in the morning

5 in the morning

6 in the evening

7 in the evening

8 in the morning

Today I scored ____ out of 8.

Year 3 Maths — Autumn Term

Week 8 — Day 3

Write the time shown on the 24-hour clock in words.

Circle to show the time of day.

03:30

half past three

in the (morning) / afternoon.

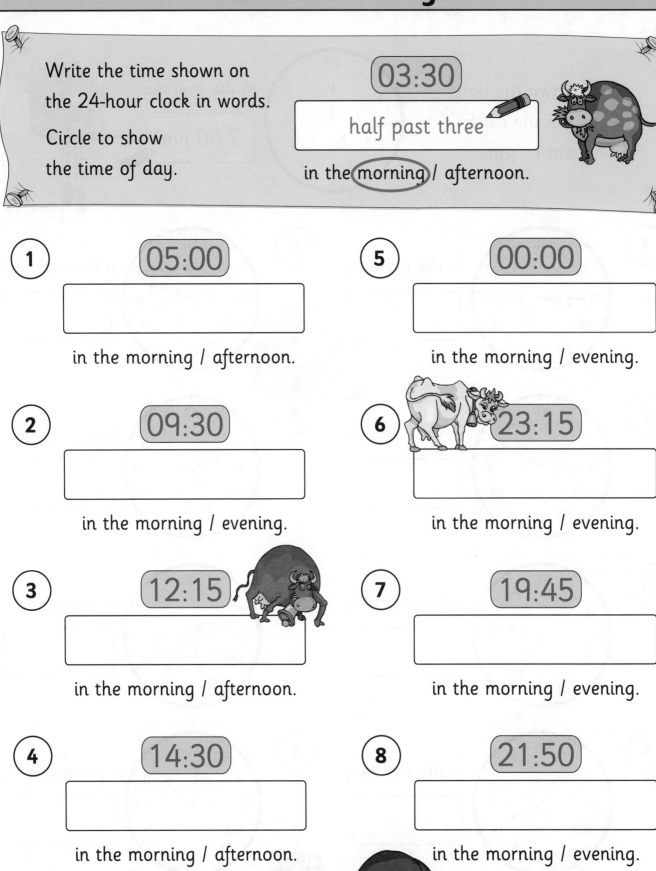

1 05:00

in the morning / afternoon.

2 09:30

in the morning / evening.

3 12:15

in the morning / afternoon.

4 14:30

in the morning / afternoon.

5 00:00

in the morning / evening.

6 23:15

in the morning / evening.

7 19:45

in the morning / evening.

8 21:50

in the morning / evening.

Today I scored [ ] out of 8.

Week 8 — Day 4

The table shows how long it took 3 people to run a race. Circle the name of the winner. Write how many seconds faster than the slowest person the winner was.

	(Ali)	Bob	Chan
Time (in seconds)	25	30	35

10 seconds

1

	Ava	Bill	Cloe
Time (in seconds)	24	26	25

seconds

2

	Dan	Elsa	Finn
Time (in seconds)	47	45	42

seconds

3

	Gwen	Hugh	Isla
Time (in seconds)	30	47	51

seconds

4

	Jim	Jane	Jai
Time (in seconds)	57	27	41

seconds

5

	Kora	Li	Mia
Time (in seconds)	49	34	45

seconds

6

	Noah	Olga	Paul
Time (in seconds)	45	54	23

seconds

7

	Raj	Sam	Tolu
Time (in seconds)	57	56	29

seconds

8

	Vera	Will	Zara
Time (in seconds)	41	38	24

seconds

Today I scored [ ] out of 8.

Year 3 Maths — Autumn Term

Week 8 — Day 5

Jasmine counted the cars she saw on her way to school. The fraction of cars that were a certain colour is shown. How many cars were **not** this colour?

Jasmine saw 20 cars.

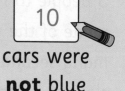

$\frac{1}{2}$ were blue   10 cars were **not** blue

1 Jasmine saw 14 cars.

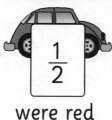

$\frac{1}{2}$ were red   ☐ cars were **not** red

2 Jasmine saw 20 cars.

$\frac{1}{4}$ were yellow   ☐ cars were **not** yellow

3 Jasmine saw 26 cars.

$\frac{2}{4}$ were pink   ☐ cars were **not** pink

4 Jasmine saw 16 cars.

$\frac{1}{4}$ were green   ☐ cars were **not** green

5 Jasmine saw 24 cars.

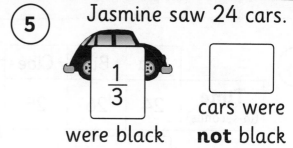

$\frac{1}{3}$ were black   ☐ cars were **not** black

6 Jasmine saw 28 cars.

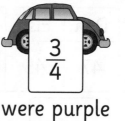

$\frac{3}{4}$ were purple   ☐ cars were **not** purple

7 Jasmine saw 33 cars.

$\frac{1}{3}$ were white   ☐ cars were **not** white

8 Jasmine saw 36 cars.

$\frac{3}{4}$ were grey   ☐ cars were **not** grey

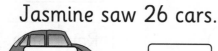

Today I scored ☐ out of 8.

Week 9 — Day 1

Fill in the box.   There are [60] minutes in an hour.

1 There are [ ] hours in a day.

2 There are [ ] hours in two days.

3 There are [ ] minutes in half an hour.

4 There are [ ] hours in half a day.

5 There are [ ] hours in a quarter of a day.

6 There are [ ] minutes in a quarter of an hour.

7 There are [ ] hours in three quarters of a day.

8 There are [ ] minutes in two hours.

9 There are [ ] minutes in one third of an hour.

10 There are [ ] minutes in three quarters of an hour.

11 There are [ ] minutes in one and a half hours.

12 There are [ ] hours in 10 days.

Today I scored [ ] out of 12.

Year 3 Maths — Autumn Term

Week 9 — Day 2

Complete the shape by joining the dots. Use a ruler.

triangle

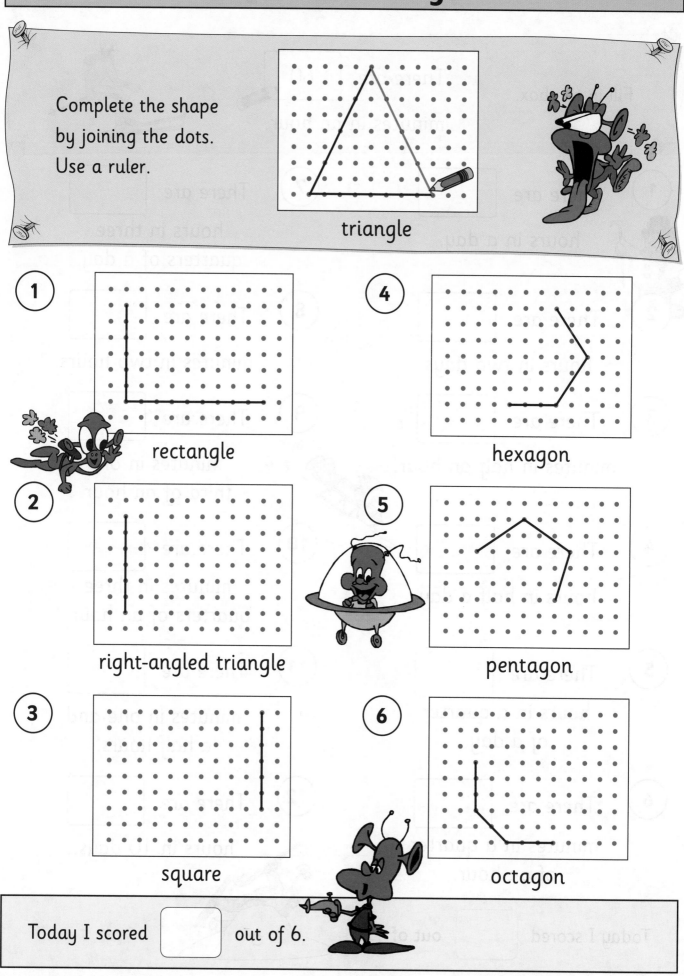

1 rectangle

2 right-angled triangle

3 square

4 hexagon

5 pentagon

6 octagon

Today I scored ☐ out of 6.

Week 9 — Day 3

Use the numbers on the cards to complete the calculation.

| 4 | 7 | 1 |

3 1 + 4 7 = 7 8

1
| 3 | 2 | 9 |

__5 + __4 = 5__

2
| 2 | 5 | 8 |

6__ + __1 = __6

3
| 6 | 8 | 1 |

__3 + 7__ = __9

4
| 1 | 3 | 2 |

__7 − __5 = 2__

5
| 2 | 3 | 9 |

5__ − __4 = __5

6
| 8 | 4 | 2 |

__4 + 6__ = __8

7
| 4 | 0 | 5 |

__4 − 1__ = 4__

8
| 3 | 7 | 2 |

__5 − 4__ = 3__

Today I scored ☐ out of 8.

Year 3 Maths — Autumn Term

Week 9 — Day 4

Circle all the shapes that match the description in the box.

| 2 or more edges |

1 | 5 or more faces

2 | 0 vertices

3 | fewer than 2 faces

4 | 6 edges or fewer

5 | 6 or more vertices

6 | 8 or more edges

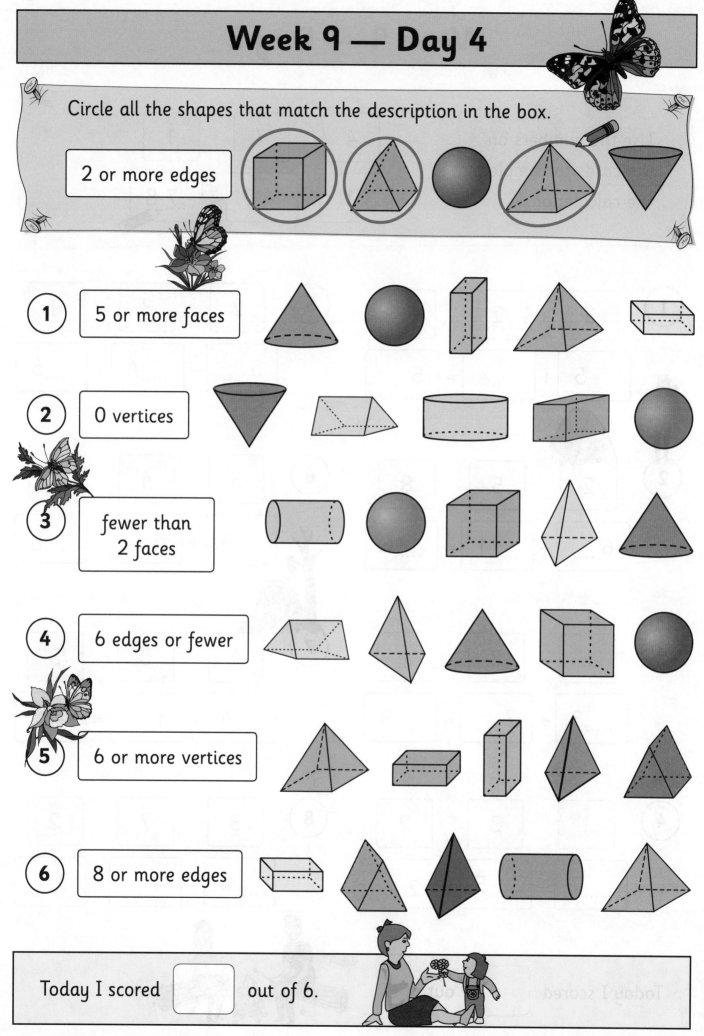

Today I scored ☐ out of 6.

Week 9 — Day 5

Each strawberry weighs **5 g**.

Write down the total weight of strawberries that Judy has left.

Judy has 10 strawberries.
She eats 3 of them.
Total weight of
strawberries left = | 35 g |

(1) Judy has 7 strawberries.
She eats 2 of them.
Total weight of
strawberries left = [g]

(2) Judy has 12 strawberries.
She eats 6 of them.
Total weight of
strawberries left = [g]

(3) Judy has 19 strawberries.
She eats 11 of them.
Total weight of
strawberries left = [g]

(4) Judy has 8 strawberries.
She eats 5 of them.
She buys 1 more strawberry.
Total weight of
strawberries left = [g]

(5) Judy has 15 strawberries.
She eats 6 of them.
Total weight of
strawberries left = [g]

(6) Judy has 25 strawberries.
She eats 14 of them.
Total weight of
strawberries left = [g]

(7) Judy has 38 strawberries.
She gives away 31 of them.
Total weight of
strawberries left = [g]

(8) Judy has 45 strawberries.
She gives away 36 of them.
She buys 3 more strawberries.
Total weight of
strawberries left = [g]

Today I scored [ ] out of 8.

Week 10 — Day 1

Grace buys sweets with a **£1 coin**.
The cost of the sweets is given.
Write how many of each coin
shown Grace was given in change.
Use as few coins as possible.

The sweets cost 82p

1 | 1

1 | 1

1 The sweets cost 67p

4 The sweets cost 76p

2 The sweets cost 23p

5

5 The sweets cost 41p

3 The sweets cost 52p

6 The sweets cost 1p

Today I scored [ ] out of 6.

Week 10 — Day 2

Write an addition you can do to check the calculation shown. Solve the addition. Circle to show whether the original answer was correct or incorrect.

$43 - 12 = 35$

| 35 | + | 12 | = | 47 |

correct   (incorrect)

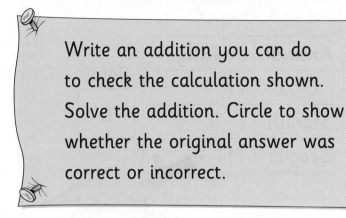

1 $56 - 24 = 32$

☐ + ☐ = ☐

correct   incorrect

2 $67 - 52 = 14$

☐ + ☐ = ☐

correct   incorrect

3 $79 - 23 = 56$

☐ + ☐ = ☐

correct   incorrect

4 $32 - 18 = 16$

☐ + ☐ = ☐

correct   incorrect

5 $94 - 69 = 25$

☐ + ☐ = ☐

correct   incorrect

6 $86 - 58 = 38$

☐ + ☐ = ☐

correct   incorrect

7 $75 - 49 = 24$

☐ + ☐ = ☐

correct   incorrect

8 $91 - 36 = 55$

☐ + ☐ = ☐

correct   incorrect

Today I scored ☐ out of 8.

Week 10 — Day 3

Cliff goes to the beach.
He records a tally of the animals he sees and he finds the total.
Fill in the missing tally marks.

Animal	Tally
Crab	I I
Starfish	I
Seagull	I I I

Total
6

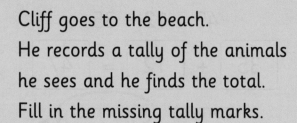

1

Animal	Tally
Crab	I I
Starfish	I I I I
Seagull	

Total
8

2

Animal	Tally
Crab	ЦНТ
Starfish	
Seagull	ЦНТ I

Total
14

3

Animal	Tally
Crab	I I
Starfish	I I I I
Seagull	

Total
11

4

Animal	Tally
Crab	
Starfish	I
Seagull	I I I I

Total
13

5

Animal	Tally
Crab	ЦНТ I I
Starfish	
Seagull	ЦНТ

Total
22

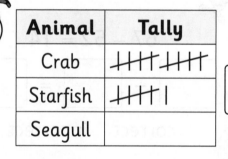

6

Animal	Tally
Crab	ЦНТ ЦНТ
Starfish	ЦНТ I
Seagull	

Total
25

7

Animal	Tally
Crab	ЦНТ I
Starfish	
Seagull	ЦНТ I I I

Total
21

8

Animal	Tally
Crab	
Starfish	ЦНТ
Seagull	ЦНТ I I

Total
23

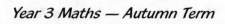

Today I scored [ ] out of 8.

Week 10 — Day 4

The table shows the number of animals in three zoos.

Circle the names of any zoos that have more than 20 animals.

Write how many more penguins than wolves are in each given zoo.

Zoo name	Tiger	Penguin	Snake	Wolf
(Milton)	2	10	5	5
Roansea	4	2	3	1
Furnside	1	0	5	2

Roansea

1

Milton

5

1

Zoo name	Tiger	Penguin	Snake	Wolf
Milton	3	8	6	6
Roansea	6	4	5	2
Furnside	1	0	7	8

Roansea

Milton

2

Zoo name	Tiger	Penguin	Snake	Wolf
Milton	0	6	7	5
Roansea	2	11	5	9
Furnside	5	8	12	6

Furnside

Milton

3

Zoo name	Tiger	Penguin	Snake	Wolf
Milton	2	12	8	0
Roansea	4	8	5	2
Furnside	0	17	23	8

Furnside

Roansea

4

Zoo name	Tiger	Penguin	Snake	Wolf
Milton	8	18	13	7
Roansea	5	19	11	11
Furnside	2	8	5	5

Roansea

Furnside

5

Zoo name	Tiger	Penguin	Snake	Wolf
Milton	3	11	5	0
Roansea	4	13	12	9
Furnside	5	8	0	7

Milton

Roansea

Today I scored [ ] out of 5.

Year 3 Maths — Autumn Term

Week 10 — Day 5

Alex had **56 crayons**. She gave some to her friends. She divided the rest equally into 3 pencil cases. How many crayons are in each pencil case?

She gave 20 to Maria and 6 to Chen.

There are ☐ 10 crayons in each pencil case.

1. She gave 6 to Abdul and 35 to Ciara.

   There are ☐ crayons in each pencil case.

5. She gave 12 to Emily and 23 to Jamal.

   There are ☐ crayons in each pencil case.

2. She gave 6 to Henry and 17 to Alika.

   There are ☐ crayons in each pencil case.

6. She gave 17 to Talia and 21 to Erik.

   There are ☐ crayons in each pencil case.

3. She gave 15 to Jade and 14 to Steve.

   There are ☐ crayons in each pencil case.

7. She gave 13 to Cesar and 7 to Niamh.

   There are ☐ crayons in each pencil case.

4. She gave 21 to Ethan and 23 to James.

   There are ☐ crayons in each pencil case.

8. She gave 19 to Aisha and 13 to Jack.

   There are ☐ crayons in each pencil case.

Today I scored ☐ out of 8.

Week 11 — Day 1

Beryl's teapot makes 3 cups of tea.
Write how many cups of tea Beryl can
make with the number of teapots shown.

6

1  ☐

2  ☐

3  ☐

4  ☐

5  ☐

6  ☐

7  ☐

8  ☐

9  ☐

10  ☐

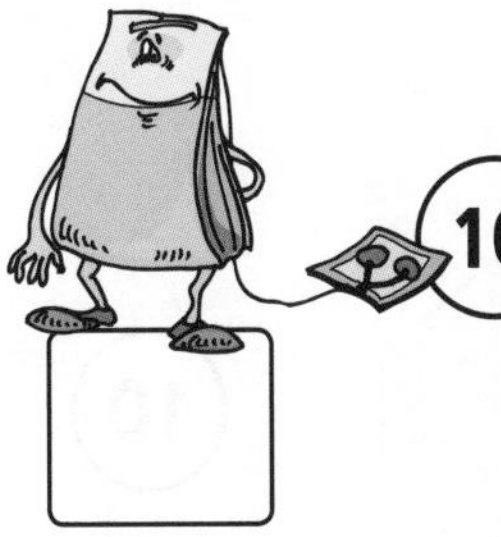

Today I scored ☐ out of 10.

Year 3 Maths — Autumn Term

Week 11 — Day 2

Circle the shape that is a hexagon.

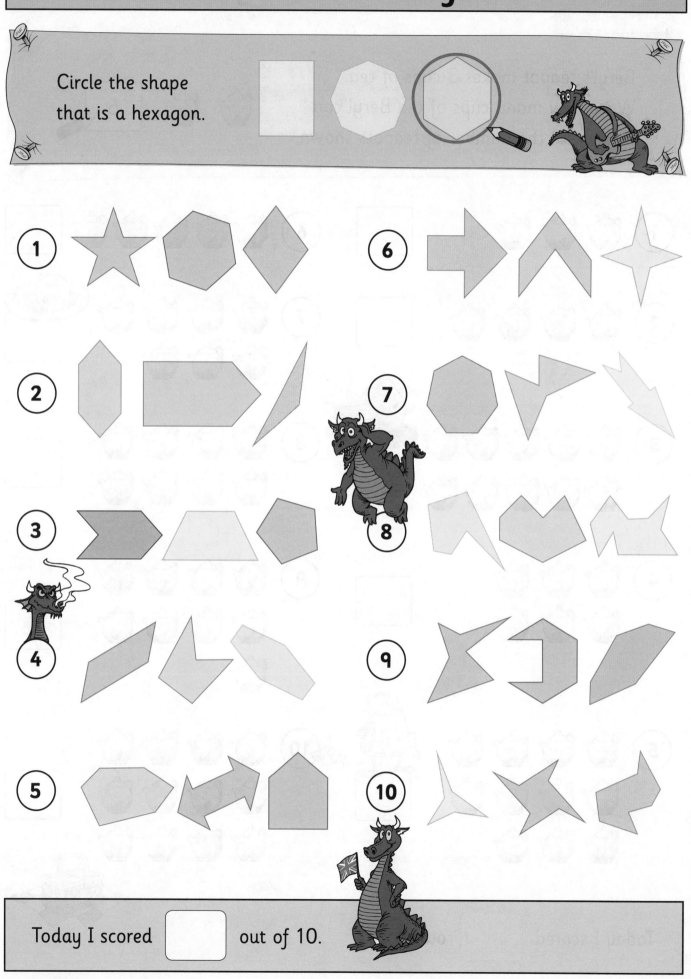

1

2

3

4

5

6

7

8

9

10

Today I scored ☐ out of 10.

Week 11 — Day 3

Fill in the missing numbers, counting in steps of four.

0   4   [8]   [12]   [16]

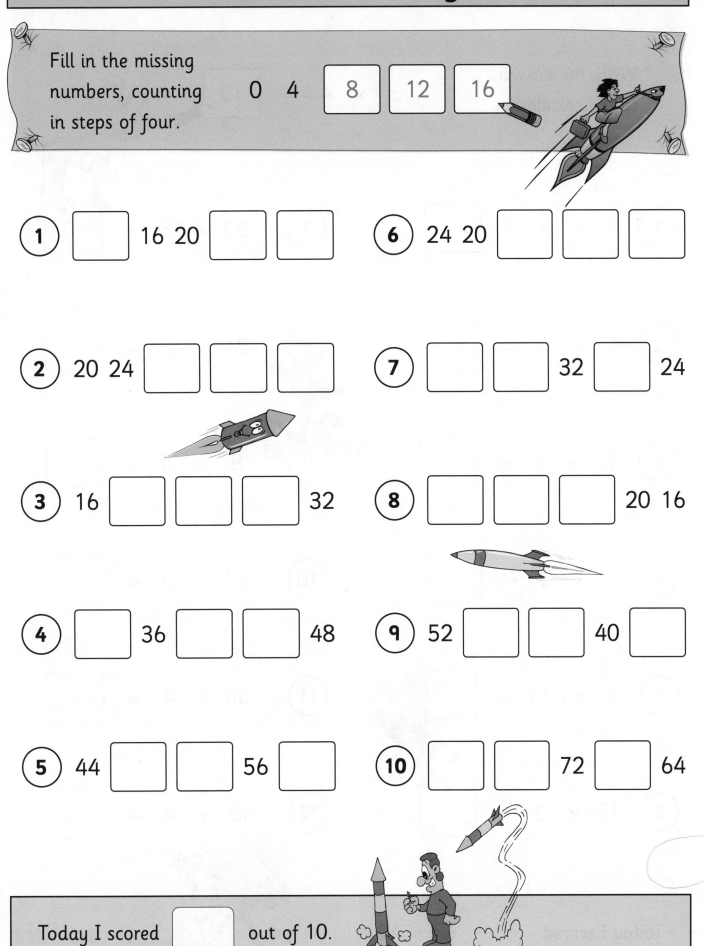

1 [ ] 16 20 [ ] [ ]

6 24 20 [ ] [ ] [ ]

2 20 24 [ ] [ ] [ ]

7 [ ] [ ] 32 [ ] 24

3 16 [ ] [ ] [ ] 32

8 [ ] [ ] [ ] 20 16

4 [ ] 36 [ ] [ ] 48

9 52 [ ] [ ] 40 [ ]

5 44 [ ] [ ] 56 [ ]

10 [ ] [ ] 72 [ ] 64

Today I scored [ ] out of 10.

Year 3 Maths — Autumn Term

Week 11 — Day 4

Write the answer to the calculation.

$3 \times 4 =$ **12**

(1) $7 \times 3 =$ ☐

(7) $33 \div 3 =$ ☐

(2) $4 \times 6 =$ ☐

(8) $24 \div 3 =$ ☐

(3) $12 \div 4 =$ ☐

(9) $8 \times 4 =$ ☐

(4) $9 \times 3 =$ ☐

(10) $27 \div 3 =$ ☐

(5) $4 \times 11 =$ ☐

(11) $36 \div 4 =$ ☐

(6) $12 \times 3 =$ ☐

(12) $48 \div 4 =$ ☐

Today I scored ☐ out of 12.

Week 11 — Day 5

Fleur picked some flowers. She picked
the number of roses shown in the box.
She picked twice as many daisies as roses.
Write how many flowers she picked in total.

1   Total: 3

1   4   Total: [ ]

2   5   Total: [ ]

3   3   Total: [ ]

4   7   Total: [ ]

5   10   Total: [ ]

6   8   Total: [ ]

7

8   12   Total: [ ]

8   11   Total: [ ]

9   9   Total: [ ]

10   13   Total: [ ]

Today I scored [ ] out of 10.

Year 3 Maths — Autumn Term

Week 12 — Day 1

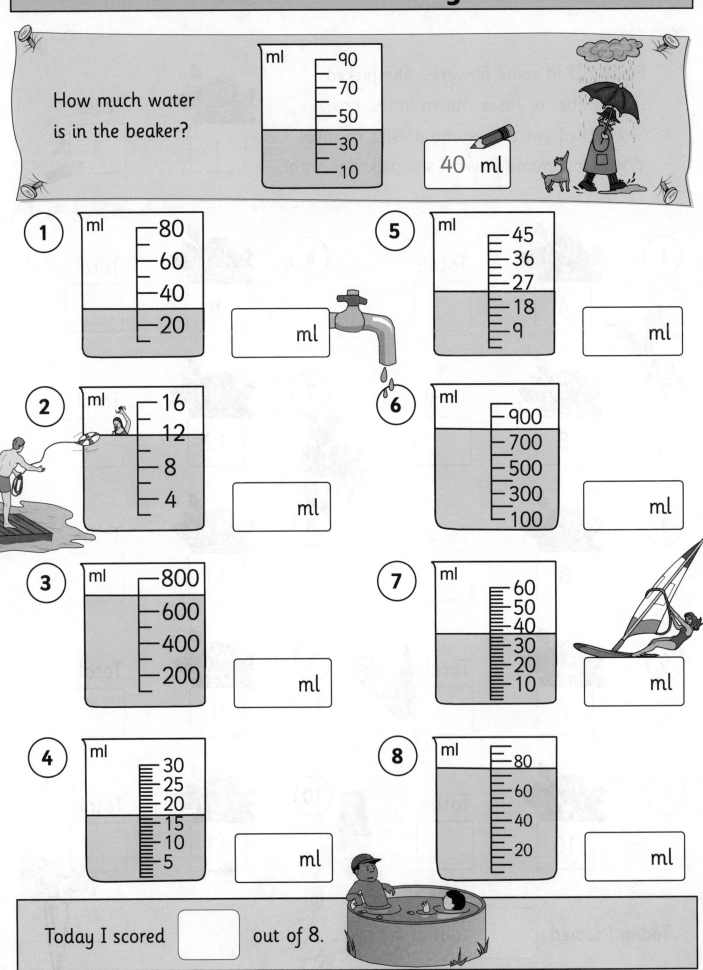

How much water is in the beaker?

40 ml

1. _____ ml

2. _____ ml

3. _____ ml

4. _____ ml

5. _____ ml

6. _____ ml

7. _____ ml

8. _____ ml

_____ ml (tap)

Today I scored [ ] out of 8.

Week 12 — Day 2

Complete the calculation.   155 + 200 = 355

(1) 202 + 200 =

(2) 356 − 100 =

(3) 580 − 200 =

(4) 592 + 300 =

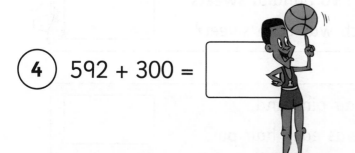

(5) 484 + 400 =

(6) 877 − 300 =

(7) 491 + 300 =

(8) 639 − 400 =

(9) 571 − 500 =

(10) 892 + 100 =

(11) 714 − 500 =

(12) 483 + 500 =

Today I scored [ ] out of 12.

Year 3 Maths — Autumn Term

58

Week 12 — Day 3

Fill in the box. | Femi has a £1 coin. He buys three biscuits and gets 40p change. How much were the biscuits? | 20p

1 Ciaran has a £1 coin. He buys two oranges and gets 80p change. How much was each orange?

2 Kelsey has a 50p coin. She buys five pencils and gets 10p change. How much was each pencil?

3 Jordan has a £1 coin. He buys 10 ice-lollies and gets 30p change. How much was each ice-lolly?

4 Raul has a 20p coin. He buys two banana sweets and gets 8p change. How much was each sweet?

5 Maeve has 66p. She buys 3 hair pins and gets 51p change. How much was each hair pin?

6 Sadio has a 89p. He buys three chocolate bars and gets 50p change. How much was each chocolate bar?

7 Lilith has 75p. She buys four stickers and gets 27p change. How much was each sticker?

Today I scored [ ] out of 7.

Year 3 Maths — Autumn Term

© CGP — Not to be photocopied

Week 12 — Day 4

Complete the calculation.

$257 - 30 =$ $\boxed{227}$

1 $355 - 20 =$ ☐

7 $244 - 50 =$ ☐

2 $486 - 40 =$ ☐

8 $639 - 50 =$ ☐

3 $582 - 50 =$ ☐

9 $846 - 70 =$ ☐

4 $753 - 40 =$ ☐

10 $862 - 80 =$ ☐

5 $881 - 70 =$ ☐

11 $454 - 90 =$ ☐

6 $327 - 30 =$ ☐

12 $338 - 80 =$ ☐

 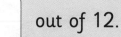 

Today I scored ☐ out of 12.

Year 3 Maths — Autumn Term

Week 12 — Day 5

Complete the calculation.

$175 +$ ⟨200⟩ $= 375$

(1) $155 + 40 =$ ▢

(2) $525 + 40 =$ ▢

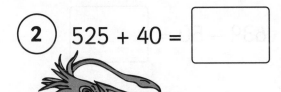

(3) ▢ $+ 50 = 380$

(4) $360 -$ ▢ $= 260$

(5) $782 -$ ▢ $= 712$

(6) $379 + 300 =$ ▢

(7) ▢ $+ 20 = 210$

(8) $736 - 400 =$ ▢

(9) $892 - 500 =$ ▢

(10) $876 +$ ▢ $= 926$

(11) ▢ $+ 90 = 584$

(12) $958 -$ ▢ $= 258$

Today I scored ▢ out of 12.

Answers

Week 1 — Day 1

1.	37	5.	19	9.	70
2.	38	6.	33	10.	7
3.	57	7.	30	11.	18
4.	12	8.	52	12.	39

Week 1 — Day 2

Week 1 — Day 3

1. cuboid, 8 vertices
2. square-based pyramid, 5 vertices
3. cone, 1 vertex
4. triangular prism, 6 vertices
5. sphere, 0 vertices
6. cuboid, 8 vertices
7. triangular prism, 6 vertices
8. cylinder, 0 vertices

Week 1 — Day 4

1. 12 kg, 25 kg, 53 kg, 91 kg
2. 49 kg, 55 kg, 74 kg, 89 kg
3. 17 kg, 25 kg, 62 kg, 72 kg
4. 20 kg, 35 kg, 47 kg, 98 kg
5. 19 kg, 40 kg, 52 kg, 78 kg
6. 13 kg, 21 kg, 38 kg, 68 kg
7. 48 kg, 83 kg, 92 kg, 97 kg
8. 29 kg, 54 kg, 73 kg, 81 kg

Week 1 — Day 5

1.	10	5.	18	9.	60
2.	60	6.	25	10.	110
3.	15	7.	22		
4.	70	8.	100		

Week 2 — Day 1

1.	$\frac{3}{4}$	6.	$\frac{3}{4}$
2.	$\frac{1}{2}$	7.	$\frac{1}{2}$
3.	$\frac{1}{4}$	8.	$\frac{1}{3}$
4.	$\frac{1}{2}$	9.	$\frac{1}{3}$
5.	$\frac{1}{3}$	10.	$\frac{3}{4}$

Week 2 — Day 2

1. 44, 34, 24, **14**, **4**
2. 25, 20, 15, **10**, **5**
3. 6, 9, 12, **15**, **18**
4. 30, 28, 26, **24**, **22**
5. 72, 70, **68**, **66**, 64
6. 27, 30, **33**, **36**, 39
7. 71, **61**, **51**, 41, 31
8. 95, **90**, 85, 80, **75**
9. **89**, 79, 69, **59**, 49
10. **36**, 38, **40**, 42, 44

Week 2 — Day 3

1. lighter, weight difference = 34 g
2. heavier, weight difference = 42 g
3. lighter, weight difference = 7 g
4. heavier, weight difference = 6 g
5. lighter, weight difference = 29 g
6. heavier, weight difference = 25 g

Week 2 — Day 4

1.	7	5.	10	9.	15
2.	8	6.	10	10.	21
3.	9	7.	15	11.	17
4.	12	8.	17	12.	24

Week 2 — Day 5

1.	3	5.	10	9.	9
2.	5	6.	8	10.	12
3.	4	7.	7		
4.	6	8.	11		

Week 3 — Day 1

1. 15, 11, 17, 19
2. 39, 17
3. 31
4. 51
5. 33, 59
6. 57, 71, 35
7. 91, 73
8. 95
9. 53, 39, 75
10. 77

Week 3 — Day 2

1.	26, 34	6.	25, 54
2.	37, 47	7.	45, 85
3.	77, 68	8.	96, 62
4.	82, 98	9.	49, 5
5.	91, 74	10.	50, 88

Week 3 — Day 3

1. 25 – 14 = 11
2. 34 – 12 = 22
3. 45 – 25 = 20
4. 50 – 37 = 13
5. 62 – 33 = 29
6. 77 – 28 = 49
7. 82 – 55 = 27
8. 94 – 69 = 25

Week 3 — Day 4

1.	10	5.	6	9.	9
2.	2	6.	4	10.	18
3.	2	7.	4		
4.	3	8.	8		

Week 3 — Day 5

1.	10	3.	16	5.	22
2.	14	4.	20	6.	24

Week 4 — Day 1

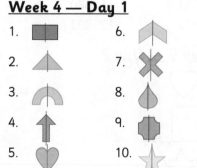

Week 4 — Day 2

1. hundreds = 100, tens = 60
2. hundreds = 300, tens = 40
3. hundreds = 500, tens = 20
4. hundreds = 200, tens = 70
5. hundreds = 400, tens = 30
6. hundreds = 100, tens = 20
7. hundreds = 600, tens = 10
8. hundreds = 700, tens = 90
9. hundreds = 400, tens = 50
10. hundreds = 800, tens = 40
11. hundreds = 900, tens = 80
12. hundreds = 700, tens = 0

Week 4 — Day 3

1. 432, 556, 698, 905
2. 249, 327, 646, 920
3. 270, 579, 717, 919
4. 259, 409, 463, 507
5. 733, 798, 978, 996
6. 295, 794, 918, 937
7. 228, 244, 511, 747
8. 587, 633, 634, 766

Week 4 — Day 4

1. 25 g
2. 35 g
3. 45 g
4. 200 g
5. 250 g
6. 50 g
7. 350 g
8. 450 g

Week 4 — Day 5

1. 11
2. 16
3. 26
4. 31
5. 41
6. 36
7. 21
8. 1
9. 46
10. 51

Week 5 — Day 1

1. 242
2. 176
3. 342
4. 103
5. 451
6. 908
7. 965
8. 611
9. 724
10. 539
11. 380
12. 893

Week 5 — Day 2

1. , pink
2. , blue
3. ☆ , blue
4. ⬠ , purple
5. ✚ , pink
6. ▢ , purple

Week 5 — Day 3

1. $37 + 22 = \mathbf{30 + 7 + 20 + 2 = 59}$
2. $41 + 46 = \mathbf{40 + 1 + 40 + 6 = 87}$
3. $32 + 23 = \mathbf{30 + 2 + 20 + 3 = 55}$
4. $85 + 14 = \mathbf{80 + 5 + 10 + 4 = 99}$
5. $63 + 17 = \mathbf{60 + 3 + 10 + 7 = 80}$
6. $81 + 27 = \mathbf{80 + 1 + 20 + 7 = 108}$
7. $34 + 86 = \mathbf{30 + 4 + 80 + 6 = 120}$
8. $69 + 99 = \mathbf{60 + 9 + 90 + 9 = 168}$

Week 5 — Day 4

1. (number line 700–900)
2. (number line 100–300)
3. (number line 100–300)
4. (number line 500–700)
5. (number line 100–300)
6. (number line 400–600)
7. (number line 600–800)
8. (number line 800–1000)

Week 5 — Day 5

1. 20
2. 23
3. 17
4. 24
5. 15
6. 17

Week 6 — Day 1

1. ◀
2. ▶
3. △
4. (shape)
5. (shape)
6. (shape)
7. (shape)
8. (shape)
9. (shape)
10. (shape)

Week 6 — Day 2

1. 694
2. 156
3. 430
4. 395
5. 779
6. 551
7. 229
8. 659
9. 118
10. 325
11. 608
12. 796

Week 6 — Day 3

1. 100
2. 10
3. 100
4. 10
5. 100
6. 10
7. 100
8. 10
9. 100
10. 100
11. 10
12. 100, 10

Week 6 — Day 4

1. (clock)
2. (clock)
3. (clock)
4. (clock)
5. (clock)
6. (clock)
7. (clock)
8. (clock)

Week 6 — Day 5

1. 1 child
2. 0 children
3. 8 children
4. 2 children
5. 3 children
6. 6 children

Week 7 — Day 1

1. 238
2. 524
3. 107
4. 450
5. 43
6. 515
7. 607
8. 193
9. 396
10. 843

Week 7 — Day 2

1. 12 cm
2. 9 cm
3. 10 cm
4. 35 cm
5. 12 cm
6. 8 cm
7. 11 cm
8. 8 cm

Week 7 — Day 3

1. smallest = 128
   largest = 982
2. smallest = 236
   largest = 763
3. smallest = 455
   largest = 855
4. smallest = 123
   largest = 932
5. smallest = 335
   largest = 753
6. smallest = 122
   largest = 522
7. smallest = 134
   largest = 643
8. smallest = 179
   largest = 997

Week 7 — Day 4

1. Any 2 sections, e.g.
2. Any 1 or 2 sections, e.g.
3. Any 1 section, e.g.
4. Any 6 sections, e.g.
5.
6. Any 1 section, e.g.
7. Any 9 to 11 sections, e.g.
8. Any 1 section, e.g.
9. Any 3 or more sections, e.g.
10. Any 6 or more sections, e.g.

Week 7 — Day 5

1. 300 ml   5. 280 l
2. 650 l   6. 770 l
3. 440 ml   7. 430 ml
4. 860 ml   8. 499 ml

Week 8 — Day 1

1. III   6. X
2. V   7. VII
3. IV   8. XI
4. VI   9. IX
5. VIII   10. XII

Week 8 — Day 2

1. 8.45 pm   5. 12.12 am
2. 10.10 pm   6. 9.34 pm
3. 2.25 am   7. 6.23 pm
4. 3.55 am   8. 1.59 am

Week 8 — Day 3

1. five o'clock, morning
2. half past nine, morning
3. quarter past twelve, afternoon
4. half past two, afternoon
5. twelve o'clock / midnight, morning
6. quarter past eleven, evening
7. quarter to eight, evening
8. ten to ten, evening

Week 8 — Day 4

1. Ava, 2   5. Li, 15
2. Finn, 5   6. Paul, 31
3. Gwen, 21   7. Tolu, 28
4. Jane, 30   8. Zara, 17

Week 8 — Day 5

1. 7   5. 16
2. 15   6. 7
3. 13   7. 22
4. 12   8. 9

Week 9 — Day 1

1. 24   7. 18
2. 48   8. 120
3. 30   9. 20
4. 12   10. 45
5. 6   11. 90
6. 15   12. 240

Week 9 — Day 2

1.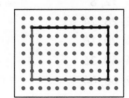

2. Must have 1 right angle and 3 sides, e.g: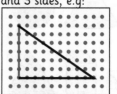
3.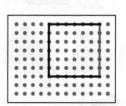
4. Must have 6 sides, e.g: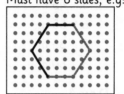
5. Must have 5 sides, e.g: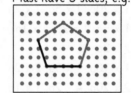
6. Must have 8 sides, e.g: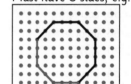

Week 9 — Day 3

1. **25 + 34 = 59** or **35 + 24 = 59**
2. **65 + 21 = 86**
3. **13 + 76 = 89**
4. **37 − 15 = 22**
5. **59 − 34 = 25** or **59 − 24 = 35**
6. **24 + 64 = 88**
7. **54 − 10 = 44**
8. **75 − 43 = 32** or **75 − 42 = 33**

Week 9 — Day 4

1.
2.
3.

Answers

4.
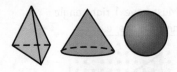

5.
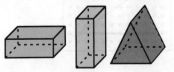

6.
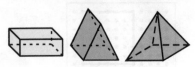

Week 9 — Day 5

1. 25 g   5. 45 g
2. 30 g   6. 55 g
3. 40 g   7. 35 g
4. 20 g   8. 60 g

Week 10 — Day 1

1. 1 x 20p, 1 x 10p, 1 x 2p, 1 x 1p
2. 1 x 50p, 1 x 20p, 1 x 5p, 1 x 2p
3. 2 x 20p, 1 x 5p, 1 x 2p, 1 x 1p
4. 2 x 10p, 2 x 2p
5. 2 x 20p, 1 x 10p, 1 x 5p, 2 x 2p
6. 1 x 50p, 2 x 20p, 4 x 2p, 1 x 1p

Week 10 — Day 2

1. 32 + 24 = 56, correct
2. 14 + 52 = 66, incorrect
3. 56 + 23 = 79, correct
4. 16 + 18 = 34, incorrect
5. 25 + 69 = 94, correct
6. 38 + 58 = 96, incorrect
7. 24 + 49 = 73, incorrect
8. 55 + 36 = 91, correct

Week 10 — Day 3

1. Seagull = ||
2. Starfish = |||
3. Seagull = ||||
4. Crab = |||| |||
5. Starfish = |||| ||||
6. Seagull = |||| ||||
7. Starfish = |||| ||
8. Crab = |||| |||| |

Week 10 — Day 4

1. Milton has more than 20 animals.
   Roansea = 2
   Milton = 2

2. Roansea and Furnside have more
   than 20 animals.
   Furnside = 2
   Milton = 1

3. Milton and Furnside have more than
   20 animals.
   Furnside = 9
   Roansea = 6
4. Milton and Roanside have more
   than 20 animals.
   Roansea = 8
   Furnside = 3
5. Roansea has more than 20 animals.
   Milton = 11
   Roansea = 4

Week 10 — Day 5

1. 5   5. 7
2. 11   6. 6
3. 9   7. 12
4. 4   8. 8

Week 11 — Day 1

1. 9   6. 15
2. 12   7. 21
3. 30   8. 24
4. 18   9. 27
5. 33   10. 36

Week 11 — Day 2

1.   6.
2.   7.
3.   8.
4.   9.
5.   10.

Week 11 — Day 3

1. **12**, 16, 20, **24**, 28
2. 20, 24, **28**, **32**, **36**
3. 16, **20**, **24**, **28**, 32
4. **32**, 36, **40**, **44**, 48
5. 44, **48**, **52**, 56, **60**
6. 24, 20, **16**, **12**, **8**
7. **40**, **36**, 32, **28**, 24
8. **32**, **28**, **24**, 20, 16
9. 52, **48**, **44**, 40, **36**
10. **80**, **76**, 72, **68**, 64

Week 11 — Day 4

1. 21   7. 11
2. 24   8. 8
3. 3   9. 32
4. 27   10. 9
5. 44   11. 9
6. 36   12. 12

Week 11 — Day 5

1. 12   6. 24
2. 15   7. 36
3. 9   8. 33
4. 21   9. 27
5. 30   10. 39

Week 12 — Day 1

1. 30 ml   5. 24 ml
2. 12 ml   6. 800 ml
3. 700 ml   7. 36 ml
4. 17 ml   8. 75 ml

Week 12 — Day 2

1. 402   7. 791
2. 256   8. 239
3. 380   9. 71
4. 892   10. 992
5. 884   11. 214
6. 577   12. 983

Week 12 — Day 3

1. 10p   5. 5p
2. 8p   6. 13p
3. 7p   7. 12p
4. 6p

Week 12 — Day 4

1. 335   7. 194
2. 446   8. 589
3. 532   9. 776
4. 713   10. 782
5. 811   11. 364
6. 297   12. 258

Week 12 — Day 5

1. 195   7. 190
2. 565   8. 336
3. 330   9. 392
4. 100   10. 50
5. 70   11. 494
6. 679   12. 700

M3WAU21